T

109 Harpers Lane

Bolton BL1 6HU

ISBN   978-0-9559171-6-5

2020

www.lancashireloominary.co.uk

Lancashire Loominary

Printed by Wood Richardson

Design by DC Graphics

The Works

Paul Salveson

The Works is dedicated to my good and generous friend, the late Henry Lewis.

Many thanks to all who commented on drafts of the novel and to The Lancashire and Yorkshire Railway Society for their help with photographs of L&YR locomotives.

March 2020

"The philosophers have only *interpreted* the world, in various ways. The point, however, is to *change* it."

- Karl Marx, *Theses on Feuerbach*, 1845

Dialect Glossary

Some of the dialogue in the following chapters is in 'broad Lancashire' – dialect. It shouldn't be too difficult to follow but to help the reader here are some words that were in common use at the time.

abeawt, abeaut	about
ah, aw	I
agate (get agate)	get moving, make a start
beilin'	boiling
boggart	hobgoblin/scary creature
brid	bird
brunt	burnt
childer	children
clemmin'	hungry; starving
deawn	down
demic	a wreck (e.g. a locomotive)
eawr, eaur	our
eawt, aut	out
fain	glad
fotch	fetch
getten, geet	got
gradely	good, positive
hasta?	have you?
keaw yed	literally 'cow head', stupid person (Westhoughton)
Lanky	Lancashire speech; Lancashire & Yorkshire Railway
neaw	now
now	No
noan	none
nowt	nothing
reet	right
snap	lunch (Wigan area)
tha, thee, theaw	you
twothri (a tuthri)	two or three
wark	work
watter/wayter	water
weer	where
whoam, whum	home

Introduction

Novels shouldn't need an introduction. My defence is that the book covers aspects of real life, particularly in the 1970s and 1980s, which some people will recognise. So a word of warning. This is a work of fiction and none of the characters bear any close resemblance to anyone, living or dead. There are only two exceptions: the figures of Jimmy Reid and James Airlie, who feature in Chapter 16. However, the events described are purely fictional. There are elements of autobiography in the main character, Dave. I did a degree at Lancaster (but came out with a modest 2.1) and I worked for a short time at Horwich Loco Works in the mid-1970s.

None of Dave's exploits are based on reality. Some of the places mentioned in the story, e.g. the RMI Club (still going, I'm glad to say) do exist, others do not. For example there was never, as far as I'm aware, a 'Railwaymen's Club' in Horwich.

The back-drop to the novel is based on the campaign to halt the closure of Horwich Loco Works, in the early 1980s, with which I had some involvement. I was commissioned to do a photographic account of the campaign, by Lancashire Association of Trades Councils. It was called 'A Threat to the Community'. Most of the images are from that piece of work, some of which are on display at the excellent Horwich Heritage Centre. If anybody recognises any of the people in the photos I'd love to know who they are, and hope they don't mind being included.

Horwich itself is a small town on the edge of Greater Manchester, though most of its people still identify as Lancastrians. 'The Works' was opened by the Lancashire and Yorkshire Railway in 1885 and was closed down in 1983, leaving some residual activities in the Foundry and Spring Smithy. That has all ended as well, and the site is being re-developed for housing. The main office block, which features in the novel, is being retained.

Part of the inspiration for writing this story was finding a scrap of paper in a file about the closure campaign, during 1983. I've never been good at filing and all the stuff about the campaign to save the Works was stuffed into a single file marked 'Loco Works'. It was time for a clear out. I found a folded bit of A4 and was about to throw it into the bin when

I had second thoughts. Opening it I found a type-written poem, called 'Song for Horwich' (see the back of the book). It wasn't signed, nor dated; but it was written sometime in 1983. Whoever wrote it had some talent. I remember the poem being chalked up on a blackboard in the Works Committee offices during the campaign and I've a photo of a couple of young apprentices standing in front of it, at the time of the People's March for Jobs in May 1983, which came through Horwich. One line asks "who'll keep their pride when the Works are no more?"

I hope this story does justice to the people who lived in Horwich and worked at the Loco Works. They deserved better than they got. Had it survived a few more years, I suspect Horwich Loco Works would be building trains once again. The novel is a tale of 'what might have been' and is written to be enjoyed, with perhaps a few political lessons.

Paul Salveson

Bolton

March 2020

1

October 30th 2025:   Looking back

Stand on top of Rivington Pike, 1400' above Horwich, and look down towards the Irish Sea; you'll get a bird's eye view of what little remains of the Loco Works, stretched out along the edge of the West Lancashire Plain. On a clear day you can see Blackpool Tower and if you're really lucky, the Isle of Man.

The 'Works' was a long strip of a place, a series of huge single-storey sheds where the different stages of locomotive building took place. Beautiful machines they were – 'Highflyers' and 'Lanky Dreadnoughts', built to haul expresses from Liverpool to Manchester at speeds we can't even manage today. 'Sea Pigs' that shifted coal across the Pennines to feed the mills and little 'Pugs' that shunted dock wharves that are now apartment blocks and corporate HQs. During the war, it built tanks and guns. Thousands worked there, me being just one who passed through. 'Category 1 shopman', the lowest of the low.

Most of the Works was demolished five years ago. In its place, 'Rivington Chase'; described as "a stunning development of 2, 3 and 4 bedroom luxury dwellings, convenient for the M65, ideal for commuting to Manchester – Horwich, Greater Manchester." Even more houses have been built, some of them for the expanding number of Chinese engineers. They don't commute – they work here. Some have even settled and have become more 'Lancashire' than many of the locals. They love black pudding, tripe and cow heel.

If it wasn't for them, Horwich could be any other depressing Northern town. It took a while for things to change. It once had mills, weaving sheds, quarries and coal mines as well as railway engineering. It had its own council, a sense of pride and community. All that went in the 1990s. We got a Tesco, a retail park that you could only get to by car, and some bits of sculpture that were supposed to remind us of 'our wonderful railway heritage'.

I look back at my time on the railway with mixed feelings. All these books you see about 'the golden age of steam' are a joke. Frying eggs and bacon on loco shovels, everyone politely spoken. It wasn't like that. There were some real bastards and it was a hard world. God help you if you were black or queer. And women didn't get much of a look in. Some 'golden age'.

But I'll tell you this. I met some of the finest people I've ever known, wielding hammers, driving locos, pulling levers and shunting wagons. That was my real education and there was nothing sentimental about it.

Horwich apprentices, 1983

2

March 1978: Starting at the Works

I'd been doing Politics and History at Lancaster and was in the middle of my second year. I'd had enough. I wasn't thrown out – I chucked myself out. I was 19 and naïve. Comrade Know-it- All: the right answers, the correct line - which boiled down to revolution, now. I'd had enough of phony debates in the Socialist Society, pretentious crap about Trotsky and The Transitional Programme of the Fourth International – and things with Sylvia had come to an end. Maybe that was what really did it. I've always had a tendency to run for it when I was feeling stressed or down.

"What the fucking hell are you doing Dave?" my Politics lecturer, Ralph Hodgson asked me over a pint in the college bar, with his usual Australian subtlety. "You're on your way to a first. Why not wait for another year and then piss off if that's what you want?"

But I'd never really fitted in. Lancaster was one of the more mixed universities, I'll grant you. That's to say, it wasn't entirely populated by over-privileged southern middle class twerps. But it still felt like it was trying to be some kind of northern colonial outpost of southern academia, with its pretentiously-named 'colleges', aspiring to be a Lancashire version of Oxford or Cambridge.

It was built in the mid-60s and the architect made the unfortunate mistake of including a 14-storey high tower. According to myth it was a common shortcut to oblivion for students who'd had enough. It certainly was an ideal height to throw yourself off, with reasonable certainty that you'd be dead as soon as you hit the ground, without too much mess. I never let it get me down that much, but I could empathise with the poor buggers who were tempted. Maybe working class university students were more likely to struggle. Even at somewhere like Lancaster you were a minority. Couple that with my shyness, natural or maybe acquired, and it didn't make for a comfortable existence. And I never quite managed to get far with any of the girls, apart from a couple of brief flings, Sylvia being the most notable.

I was a signed-up member of the Communist Party and I felt in a twisted sort of way that it was my political duty to get a real job amongst real workers - the industrial working class, still making real things in real factories. Really. Was that all? Being honest with myself I knew that part of it was a retreat, going back to something familiar and comfortable. A cop-out, justified by Marxist-Leninist theoretical bullshit.

So I was glad to get out, walk down to the A6 and put my thumb out, heading home to Bolton. Only 40 miles, but a different world. I'd already sorted out a flat in Horwich that was being vacated by a mate who was moving into a bigger place. It was a small town a couple of miles outside Bolton. The flat was good enough, more room than the student bedsit I'd had in Lancaster.

Horwich was a 'railway town'. It wasn't a big place, not a Doncaster, nor a Crewe, a big village in some ways. But large enough, about 20,000 people, most of them connected with the Loco Works one way or another. The Works opened in the 1880s and at the time it was one of the most advanced railway engineering plants in the country – probably the world - attracting some talented engineers. The Lancashire and Yorkshire Railway was proud of its new factory and made sure its workers had company loyalty drilled into their bones.

Houses were built, ranging from basic two-bedroomed terraces adjoining the Works, all named after railway engineers - Webb, Trevithick, Brunel, Gooch, and the amusingly-named Siemens Street. Further up the hill were more substantial terraces with bay windows for the foremen and clerks. Then you were into the larger semi-detached villas for the managers culminating in very desirable mansions for the chiefs. In Horwich, the top dog wasn't the mayor or the vicar but The Chief Mechanical Engineer.

They didn't just provide housing. There was a Mechanics Institute with an extensive library, covering not only science and engineering but literature and philosophy. Evening classes were run for the apprentices and other workers too. Just down the road was the cottage hospital, which was kept busy with the regular accidents in the Works. One thing it didn't have was a pub; the railway company didn't like the idea of its employees getting pissed and turning up late for the morning shift. So the workers used to go up Lee Lane into the old town where there was no shortage of ale houses.

There were other bits of industry apart from the Works – the quarries and even a few coal pits that had closed well before the Second World

War. There was some cotton spinning and a bit of weaving. During the last war De Havilland opened an aircraft factory on the edge of the town, which creamed off some of the Loco Works' most skilled engineers. Better money, safer and warmer.

Nobody could say it was a pretty town but its saving grace was the moors that stretched out above it, up to Rivington Pike and Winter Hill. Between the town and open moorland was the park developed by Lord Leverhulme, 'the great philanthropist.'

Oh really? He was able to be such a generous chap because of the huge profits he made from his workers at Port Sunlight Soap Works. The suffragettes didn't think much of him either – they burnt his house down. Good for them. That was a few years after thousands of mill workers from Halliwell had marched up Winter Hill to reclaim a footpath that the even more obnoxious Colonel Ainsworth had closed off. Some sort of progress - you can walk up Winter Hill now without being attacked by gamekeepers, but watch out for the dog shit, left in small black plastic bags by their thoughtful owners.

My flat was on Lee Lane, the main street of the old town, above a grocer's shop. It was furnished, with a comfortable settee that you had trouble getting up from. There was a kitchen with a gas cooker and a small dining table for two and a tiny bedroom with a double bed squeezed in. And peering out of the bedroom window you could catch a glimpse of Rivington Pike rising up in the distance.

All I needed was a job. I rang a couple of places to see if they had anything going for unskilled labourers, as opposed to failed political scientists or critical social theorists. I tried a couple of the usual places in Bolton and got the bum's rush, then rang British Rail Engineering Limited, Horwich, as it described itself in the phone book. 'Horwich Loco' as everyone knew it. The pay was rubbish but it was handy for the flat. The bloke I spoke to in the Personnel Office was at least honest.

"Yes, we're taking on labourers. It's not easy work I have to tell you, but there is overtime and railway travel facilities after you've been with us for more than six months."

He might have added that most don't last that long; many jacked the job after a week. "Come down for your medical tomorrow morning and bring some references."

References? What were they recruiting? Atomic scientists?

That evening I went round to see my dad, still living in his council house in Great Lever where he'd been for 30 years. He'd lived on his own the last four. Mum had run off with 'Slimy Jack' Heaton, the local greengrocer and they were living in respectable lower middle class sin - they'd bought a bungalow in Lytham St Annes. Nice garden and even a 'car port'.

I told dad about my new career. He thought I'd gone mental. He'd worked all his life in Walker's Tannery and had hopes for his lad becoming 'summat in an office', at least. Maybe a teacher. Instead, I was starting at the Loco Works. What a kick in the teeth it must have been, after he'd never had chance to do anything but work in a foul-smelling soul-destroying limeyard.

"Tha'll do what tha wants to do," he told me, gazing into the fireplace. "You always were headstrong. Like your mum. Y' tek after her mooar than me. But I'll give you six months and tha'll be regrettin' it."

In the Machine Shop

When I turned up at the gatehouse the next day I was sent down to the Personnel Office and was asked to fill in a form, producing my last P45. I'd some paperwork from a summer job I did the previous year and thought I'd blag the rest. The guy on the desk was nice enough. I told him the truth about Lancaster, more or less. I said couldn't manage on a student grant and had decided to leave and just wanted something short-term to tide me over. I didn't say I was interested in the workers' overthrow of capitalism, seeing my employment at his factory as a small step in that direction. "Welcome to British Rail Engineering then, lad," he said, without any obvious irony.

I was sent for my medical and got the all-clear. I was to start on Monday morning, May 18th at 07.30. 'David Horrocks, shopman category 1. Weekly wage: bugger all'.

There was a group of ten of us gathered at the Gatehouse. Most were signed up for the Foundry, though for some reason I was being sent to the Spring Smithy, at the far end of the Works. First, we were taken back into the Personnel Office to complete more forms.

"Right, sign these – your contract of employment with BREL; your membership of the Pension Fund – and this, your union membership. You've got to be a member of either the engineering union or the railwaymen's union. Which one do you want?"

It turned out that the NUR – National Union of Railwaymen – was a few pence a week cheaper than the engineering union, so I opted for that. Not exactly a principled decision.

I was taken down to the Spring Smithy by one of the 'green card men' – mostly old blokes who had come off their proper job through ill-health or an accident and just buggered about the Works doing nothing much. They'd earned their easy jobs. My escort was Fred Ramsbottom, who spent most of his time brewing up in the Gatehouse. Horwich born and bred.

"Reet, come this way lad. Hasta bin 'ere afoor?"

"No, I've heard about it though, my uncle worked on the railway as a driver and he used to bring locos in for repair. Sometimes used to let me have a ride in the cab."

"Well tha were lucky. This is weer they used to build 'em. It oppened in 1885. Befoor then Horwich were nowt but a little village. We don't do any loco work no mooar though, that finished i' '64. It's aw wagons and coaches neaw, though we've started repairing some electrics from Liverpoo' . Reet – over theer it's th'Paint Shop. Let's walk through here an' ah'll show thi a few mooar seets as we go along here. Tha knows what this road's cawd? 'The Golden Mile'. It's over a mile long and runs from one end o'th'Works to t'other. It's a bit of a joke like."

It didn't look like any holiday resort I'd ever seen.

Spring Smithy

We walked past the Boiler Shop and Machine Shop, before Fred took me into the Erecting Shop where the main job of building locos once took place. "It's cawd Th'Wagon Shop neaw, aw they do is mend bloody wagons. A bit different from when ah worked 'ere, overhaulin' big steamers. We had to caulk th' locomotive boilers – noisy, an' heavy. If you didn't get th' boiler stays reet, th' engine wouldn't steam. That's why mi 'earin's buggered. An mi chest's noan so good noather. Probably th'asbestos though th'company never admitted responsibility. Steam loco boilers were stuffed full o' th'stuff."

Fred got plenty of 'ow do's' and 'aw reets' as we walked through the shop. Everyone knew him. He'd started here as an apprentice in 1938 but within a couple of years was called up for the army. He spent the next five years in the Lancashire Fusiliers – Egypt, Burma and other hell-holes. When he was de-mobbed there was a job waiting for him back at the Loco Works. He did another two years of his apprenticeship and was taken on as a boilersmith. I tried asking him about his war-time experiences but he just answered in monosyllables. "Aye" and "Appen" and "Ah suppose so..." He was a lot more talkative about the Works. Just like my dad who'd never talk about the war.

We passed out of the Wagon Shop and walked through the Foundry, all part of my conducted tour.

"This is a mucky 'ole, think thisel lucky they've not sent thee 'ere lad."

The Mechanised Foundry

It was a hot, noisy place for sure. Most of the work seemed to be making brake blocks for wagons, using castings that went round on a sort of belt. Unlike other parts of the Works, there were a few black faces here. Mostly Asian lads but a few Africans too. You didn't have to be time-served to work in the Foundry. The chance of getting an apprenticeship if you were black was virtually nil.

There were a few National Front leaflets, half-ripped down, on some of the walls and a chalk-written slogan saying 'Pakis Out'. So much for working class brotherhood.

We escaped from the Foundry; the Spring Smithy was nearby. "Here we are, aw'll tek thi up to th' Foreman's Office an' leave thi to it."

"Harold, aw've browt thi another slave," he said, turning round to give me a wink. "He seems a bright lad, unlike some o' th'keaw-yeds they send yo."

Harold Jepson was the day-shift foreman. He wore the standard foreman's blue smock and had a pencil in his top pocket. I'd guess he was about 60 but looked nearer 80, worn down by fags, beer and the caustic atmosphere of the Spring Smithy.

"Reet, thanks Fred. Neaw then. 'David Horrocks...cat 1 shopman.' Well then David, aw'll gi thi a little tour round the shop and show you what goes on, an' then we'll get you kitted out and get thi started."

"This is where owd wagon springs are stripped apart. Hasta seen a wagon spring? It's several leaves, or plates, on top of each other which bend under th'weight of a wagon or carriage. Same as they used to have in th'days of horse-drawn carriages, nowt changes. We strip aw th'leaves apart an' then they go into that furnace, over theer. They come out red hot. Tha mun watch thiself; we use these tongs to grip the leaf when it comes eawt. Then they get dipped into that oil bath – on them jigs - an' they come eawt good as new. They get put back together and we send 'em off to th'Wagon Shop for re-assembly."

A lot of the blokes just wore a t-shirt and jeans apart from a leather brat to give some basic protection. Overalls were too hot. As we walked along, most were engrossed in the job though some gave me a cheery nod.

It looked easy enough. The blokes on the jigs had the technique down to a fine art. When they lifted the hot piece of metal out of the jig it they gripped it with the tongs dead in the middle. It involved a mix of strength, dexterity and good judgement. The trick was to get the hot metal precisely in the middle before lifting it. If you were a fraction of an inch out it would swivel round and catch you. You'd burn.

The tour of the Smithy ended up back in the foreman's office and I was given my one item of protective clothing: a smith's apron – or 'brat' as they called it in the Smithy. It wasn't some pretty floral pinny but a well-used leather apron, encrusted with oil and dirt. I loved the feel and smell of it.

"Reet let's get thi started," said Harold Jepson. I was given the job of stacking the finished spring-leaves. It seemed easy enough at first but after a few dozen it started to ache. And there was no let up. The Smithy operated a bonus system which depended on everyone pulling their weight and if you couldn't keep up you'd be unpopular, to put it mildly. No wonder so many asked for their cards by Friday. By dinner-time I was aching all over.

Spring Smithy

I was shown where to make a brew and I'd brought some cheese sandwiches. I was joined by a couple of the lads off the jigs, Barry and Ged, a bit older than me but not much, mid 20s I'd guess.

"Everyone aches like fuck on the first couple of days," said Ged. "You'll get used to it. It's better than th'foundry."

"If they put you on th'jigs," my other new workmate, Barry, added, "for fuck's sake be careful. If the metal swivels round and catches you, it's fucking agony. It's never happened to me - yet - but I've seen it with some of the other blokes. Sometimes their arm would be half off, with the iron biting into the flesh like a hot knife going through butter. You could smell the burning flesh, like a fuckin' barbecue. They'd whisk 'em off to th' medic straight away before the ambulance arrived, and you'd not see them for a few months. Some never came back, and I can't blame 'em." Well thanks Barry, that was reassuring.

We clocked off at 4.30, I'd never felt time move so slow.

"Dosta think tha'll stick it then?" asked foreman Harold as I hung my brat up in the mess area.

"Oh aye, I'll be fine when I get used to it," I lied, just wanting to lie down and die.

What a relief it was coming out of the door and into the fresh air. It was early summer but it must have been 15 degrees cooler outside. I'd left my bike parked up by the gatehouse and I felt every inch of that Golden Mile. I got home at 5 and went straight to bed. Only the alarm clock woke me up the morning after.

I arrived just after 7, coming in at the south gatehouse this time, closer to the Smithy. I left my bike in the shelter and walked down, meeting Barry who was just in front of me.

"Aw reet Dave,we're early, let's geet a brew on."

He was from Wigan – his accent totally different from the local one - and a keen Rugby League player. He'd been signed for the Wigan junior team but couldn't put the time in between work and girlfriends.

There was a serious side to him as well. Over our dinner break we got talking about novels – I'd seen a well-thumbed copy of *Tess Of The D'Urbervilles* lying among a pile of union magazines and *Playboys* by his locker. It turned out he was a keen reader and we got into conversation about favourite novelists. He loved the classics – Dickens, Hardy and a special liking for Arnold Bennett. "I like the way he writes about th'Potteries. A bit like here in a way. He understands life, unlike that twat George Orwell who knew fuck all abeawt Wigan."

That seemed a bit unfair. I was a huge fan of Orwell and Homage to Catalonia was one of my favourites. "Aye, he were a socialist of sorts but deep down a middle class southern toff as looked down on th'likes of us, Dave."

I hadn't expected to be involved in a debate on English literature on the second day of my career at the Loco. But that was typical; you never knew what lay beneath these foul-mouthed but fundamentally decent blokes. That half-hour lunch break on Tuesday morning was the beginning of my real education.

It was a different world to Lancaster, that was for sure. The only feminine presence was a few cheesy pictures pinned up around the mess area – tits and arses, usual sort of stuff, lifted out of soft porn mags like the ones Barry kept alongside Thomas Hardy. Some of the shop stewards tried to remove them but they soon went back up. It wasn't that big a deal, at least then.

Brew time in staff 'restaurant'

I don't ever remember seeing a woman in the shop all the time I was there. That'd be about five years - when they announced they were shutting us down. A couple of women journalists popped their heads through the door during the closure campaign but they weren't allowed in, on 'safety grounds'. We had to work in the place all the time, safe or not.

There were a few women employed at the Works, mainly in the canteen and offices. The Typing Pool was an all-female enclave ruled over by Mrs Watson, a lady of indeterminate age and a great fat backside, possessed of a furious temper. Her 'young ladies' were mostly lasses who had just left school, though there were a few who had come back after having kids. Normally the offices would be out of bounds to us shopmen. You'd only see the corridors of power if you were in trouble, attending a disciplinary.

After a few weeks I'd had enough of stacking wagon springs and was relieved when Harold came along and asked if I fancied doing 'a bit o' striking'. This seemed an odd request but it wasn't about mounting a picket line but working as a blacksmith's assistant. The smith would hold the hot metal by a small pair of tongs and his 'striker' would hit it with a big hammer. Again, it was more difficult than it looked and I was put to work with Sam Baines, a miserable ill-tempered old bugger at the best of times. "Hit the bloody thing square on lad," he implored. After missing a couple more times, nearly hitting him instead of the metal, he threw his hands up in disgust.

"Tha's not med out for this lad."

But I was in luck. There was a vacancy on the jigs after one of the lads had got a nasty burn and was off sick. I'd be working with Barry and Ged so I was up for it. My attempts at using the tongs were more successful than my short time as a blacksmith's striker. I got the hang of catching the hot metal dead centre and lifting it out of the jig. We could have a laugh and the time went pretty quickly.

Like lots of places that were hell to work in, there was a camaraderie in the Spring Smithy. I soon got to know the other blokes doing different jobs around the shop, as well as Barry and Ged. We'd look out for each other and share our snap if some of the men's wives were more generous with the sandwiches. If someone dropped a bollock that might have got him in trouble, we'd do our best to cover. And the foremen were mostly OK. As long as the job got done and the bonus targets were met, they were happy. And so were we. That's why we took risks and cut corners so we'd get finished earlier, while the poor bastards in The Foundry had to work right up to the clock.

Mechanised Foundry

I was the youngest bloke in the shop so occasionally I got asked to do bits of jobs around the Works. It was helped by having my bike on hand, so I could nip down to the office with messages and be back in a few minutes, instead of taking an hour to walk there and back. My adventures started one morning when I was on the day shift.

3

April 1978: The Typing Pool

"Dave lad, willta nip down to th' offices and take this sheet in for typing?" Harold Jepson had a typewriter of his own in the office but he couldn't use it to save his life. I suppose I could have offered to do it myself but it wasn't my job and I was a paid up union member now. And a few minutes away from the jigs was no bad thing anyway. "And don't get up to owt with those lasses while you're down there..."

I jumped on the bike and pedalled off down The Golden Mile, calling in at the Machine Shop for a quick chat with Jim Lee, a fellow party member. "Where are you off too then, had enough o'th' Smithy then?" he asked, stuffing a few copies of *The Morning Star* into my saddlebag. "No, being the delivery lad today Jim – see you at the meeting tonight then."

I left the bike outside the offices and walked up the stairs into the main corridor. The Typing Pool was somewhere down on the right, I'd been advised. The sign on the door, typed in neat block capitals, said 'TYPING POOL – KINDLY KNOCK BEFORE ENTERING'. So I did and walked in. My entry provoked a hush, as the machine-gun rapping of the typewriters momentarily ceased.

"Continue your work girls," boomed Mrs Watson. "Haven't you seen a young man before, even if he is a particularly dirty specimen?"

And I was a bit mucked up I have to admit. The Spring Smithy was hardly a clean and tidy place - oil and shit were everywhere.

"I've a sheet for typing from Harold Jepson," I said, without deferring to the tyrant.

The Typing Pool

 "Thank you, I shall see that one of my ladies attends to it in duc course. Good day."

Later that afternoon Harold Jepson shouted across to me: "I've just had a call from th'Typing Pool, th'letter's ready. Get on your bike and collect it for us willta?"

I was down in five minutes and this time there was no sign of Mrs Watson. Instead one of the older women from the pool came up to me and said "Your typing's nearly ready son, do you want a cup of tea while you're waiting?"

That was an offer I couldn't refuse, smithy work is hot, thirsty stuff and any time I could scrounge away from the jigs was a bonus. While she was brewing up I noticed a copy of *TSSA Journal* on her desk, the magazine for the 'white collar' railway union.

She came back with the tea – a big mug for me and a more dainty cup and saucer for herself. She was a good-looking woman in her early 40s,

I guessed. Black hair tied back in a bun, wearing a figure-hugging skirt and top. Lipstick, and make-up, but not overdone.

"Sit down then, we won't eat you," she told me. "I'm Midge by the way."

"Thanks....I'm Dave. So are you involved in the union then?" I asked, pointing to the union paper.

"I'm the office rep, for what it's worth. Most of the girls are in the union, though not exactly militant. My mum and dad were both union people, as well as my late husband."

"Oh, sorry..."

"No need to be sorry lad, it was years' ago. Accident in the Wagon Shop. Nobody's fault. And the union fought for a good compensation deal, not that it could bring him back. So are you involved in union stuff?"

"Well, I'm interested," I replied. "But if I've only been here a few weeks. The guys on the branch committee have been here for decades. And I don't know whether I'll stick it, to be honest. "

"Yes, most of the lads who work in the Smithy last a few months, some less. Hard work and low pay, isn't it?"

"Yeah, but it's a job and pays the rent. And it's experience. Nice blokes to work with, mostly. A few racists, but you get that everywhere."

"Aye, and some of the attitudes towards woman are from the Stone Age too. Even the so-called 'union men'. But anyway, here's Sonia with your typing."

I got a nice wink from Sonia and a smile from Midge. "Maybe see you on a picket line, then?"

I got back to the foreman's office with an exasperated-looking Jepson. "Where the fuck have you bin? Tha's bin gone over a fuckin' hour."

"Sorry Mr Jepson, I'm afraid I got a puncture and it took me a while to get it up."

 "Aye, ah bet it did – get back to th' jigs. Next time ah'll goo misel."

4

April 1978: The Communist Party in session

The Horwich Communist Party branch didn't have that many members but there was one particular comrade towards whom I harboured more than purely comradely intentions. Judy Aspinall. Like most political parties, the CP was seen as a good place to meet attractive members of the opposite sex. After my failed attempts at Lancaster, I had pretty much a clear field in the Horwich branch, as the next youngest male comrade was in his late 50s. Judy was doing Sociology at Bristol and was back at her parents for a few weeks over the summer holidays.

Her parents lived on the private estate on the edge of town, whence many of the wage slaves at 'the loco' aspired to retire, if they got enough overtime in. They were typical *Daily Mail* readers, perhaps in my prejudiced eyes. He was a clerk in the Works offices and had risen to the dizzy heights of Clerical Officer 3, after 30 years railway service. Chairman of the Conservative Club and played golf every Saturday. Mum stayed at home and went slowly round the bend, getting pissed on cheap whisky. I somehow doubt that Judy told them that she was a card-carrying member of the Communist Party of Great Britain.

We'd already exchanged looks at the meeting last month, during a particularly dull talk on 'Prospects for World Peace and the Leading Role of the Soviet Union' given by one of the more Stalinist comrades on the district committee. The prospects for us being more than just good comrades looked good, even if those for world peace didn't, and I was hoping she'd be there tonight.

The meeting started at 7.30, in the Railwaymen's Club. It normally lasted about two hours but had the potential of feeling like six. It was advertised as a 'film show' – 'My Two Weeks' Holiday in Socialist Bulgaria' by another of the hacks from the branch committee, Albert Ackroyd. Fitter in the Erecting Shop. Another old Stalinist whose main contribution to the class struggle was using up his railway passes to visit 'socialist paradises' such as Czechoslovakia, the Soviet Union, GDR and the rest of them. He'd come back full of it. "There's no litter, you can eat in a workers' restaurant for less than five bob – and the beer is so cheap too."

He might have added that the KGB were such nice blokes, always ready with a laugh and a joke in between torturing you if you upset the regime. The Prague Spring, Hungary and Perestroika had passed him by. The world was changing and our party was moving towards 'Eurocommunism' – communism with a smiley liberal face. Albert and the old guard would have none of it. He'd rant about 'bourgeois revisionism' and even worse, 'right-wing deviationism'. It was like the Spanish Inquisition. I could imagine Albert torturing 'deviationists' in the Foundry with hot irons – "Do you renounce the devil, Leon Trotsky, and all his works?"

They weren't all like that. George Cannon, who worked in the Boiler Shop, was older than most of them and had lived through the Second World War and served with the SAS in Yugoslavia. He'd stories about fighting with the Partisans and kept in touch with many of his old Yugoslav comrades. But he could see the world was changing and the old Soviet regime was bankrupt. I learnt a lot from George. I remember him telling me about a beautiful Yugoslav Partisan girl he fell in love with. The Nazis got her and that was the end of that. He got married when he came home but I wonder how much he still thought about his lovely partisan comrade. He once showed me a photograph of her, looking gorgeous - a machine gun by her side and a sexy smile. Even partisans wore lipstick.

The club was down Station Street. What a dump it was. It reeked of stale beer and piss and was the last place on this earth where I'd willingly spend any time. The club regulars didn't like us commies meeting there but we were tolerated because we bought some of their disgusting keg beer. For us, Jim Lee insisted we should meet there because "that was where the workers gathered."

What a load of crap, Jim, nice guy that you are. Most of them hadn't worked for years, taking the money when they got the chance, either redundancy or some sort of ill-health pay-off, usually caused by fags and ale. And as for class consciousness, they were hardly conscious before they'd had their first pint, and usually lost it pretty soon after.

I arrived a bit late and my luck was in. Judy had got there just before me and was sat towards the back of the room. After 'minutes of the last meeting' we were treated to a few words from our comrade chairman – Eric Longstaff, coppersmith in the Erecting Shop.

"Comrades, welcome to tonight's meeting which is of particular interest to those of us who recognise the great achievements of the socialist countries. I am delighted that Comrade Ackroyd has agreed to give an illustrated talk on his recent holiday, with his good lady wife, in Socialist Bulgaria. I am aware that some of our younger comrades think it is the 'in' thing to scorn the achievements of the socialist countries but I trust that Comrade Ackroyd's talk will shed some fascinating light on life in today's socialist Bulgaria. Comrade, please begin. And could someone turn the lights off please?"

I was sat next to Judy and got a very nice smile from her when I came in. We whispered some quick helloes and shared some wry glances during comrade Longstaff's introduction.

The slide show was predictably tedious. "The next twenty slides are of our escorted visit to the No. 25 Tractor Factory in Dimitrovgrad...we were honoured to be met by the Works Committee of the factory who displayed their customary socialist hospitality...."

But it worked to my advantage. I could tell that Judy was as bored as I was so I thought well, nothing ventured...I gently placed my hand on her knee and gave it a gentle squeeze. No immediate reaction, but no brush off either. Then her hand on top of mine.

After a few minutes I moved up her leg a bit further and got a very cheeky grin, just made out through the light from the next lot of slides about the wonderful workers' holiday camp. I moved my hand further up, touching the edge of her knickers. But that was as far as she'd go, pushing my hand back down her leg, giving it a little comradely squeeze as she did.

I made a token attempt to recapture lost ground but she wasn't having it. Just as well, as the lights suddenly came back on.

"Well thank you comrades, I hope you found that enlightening and instructive. Could we now have questions?"

Silence.

"Comrade Horrocks at the back, you look particularly moved by the proceedings, is there anything you would like to ask of our speaker?"

"Oh, errr thank you comrade. What a very enlightening contribution that was...I feel positively excited and inspired. So yes, a question for Comrade Ackroyd. Would you say that there are any lessons for British workers from the experience of socialism in Bulgaria?"

I thought that was pretty good in the circumstances, not helped by the giggles from Judy next to me. I haven't a clue what the reply was but it got me off the hook.

"Well if there is no AOB I will declare the meeting closed. As you know it's local elections next month and as we agreed at the previous meeting we will not stand any candidates. So comrades are urged to support the Labour Party. In closing the meeting I thank you all for your attendance. If any comrade wishes to partake of some liquid refreshment in the bar, we can continue our discussion there."

Like fuck we will I thought. I'd had enough of a politics that felt like a throw-back to the 1950s. I began to long for our crazy far-left debates at Lancaster. What's more it was coming up to 9.00 and I had high hopes of unfinished business with Judy.

"Would you like me to walk you home?"

"Well that is very gallant of you, comrade," Judy smiled, "if it isn't too much trouble."

"Not at all. Perhaps we can discuss this year's grain harvest in the Urals on our way back."

We said good night to the comrades and headed down Siemens Street towards Judy's parents. The street's name always made me laugh. It's a quiet side street off the main Bolton Road with a ginnel running down to the Works. Siemens was one of the railway engineers after whom these streets, built by the railway company, were named. Most of its residents were unaware of this historical fact and felt slightly dubious about living in a street whose name could be mis-interpreted. But attempts to persuade the council to change it for something less embarrassing were unsuccessful. "We must respect the town's historical heritage," the planning officer told the residents. Or just too much bother.

Part of Horwich's historical heritage was young apprentices and shop lads taking their girls down a ginnel for a kiss, grope and whatever they could get away with. I tried my best to perpetuate the tradition but didn't get very far.

"Sorry Dave, mum and dad are expecting me back and I'd be in enough trouble if they knew where I'd been, let alone doing this."

"OK, perhaps some other time?"

"Mmm..maybe. But I'm going back to uni in a week so we've not much time."

We got to her house and said our goodbyes. "Well thank you for a very instructive and educational evening comrade," I said to her. "The pleasure has been all mine... comrade."

5

....a few days later

It was just after half-past seven on a Monday night and I was hungry. I'd started to get used to work in the Smithy but it gave me a massive thirst - and appetite. After two pizzas in succession earlier in the week I decided to opt for the chip shop down Chorley New Road. I'd always liked cooking when I was at Lancaster but I was just too knackered after a day's work to be bothered. I got the bike out and pedalled off.

It wasn't the best chippy in the world, but it was handy. I set my heart on fish, chips and peas, with a buttered flour cake, which is Bolton-ese for 'bread roll'.

I chained the bike to a drain-pipe and walked in, to find Midge at the counter, waiting for her supper.

"Hello, brother, fancy seeing you here."

"Hi...it's Midge, isn't it. Hello again."

"I hope your typing was OK?"

"Apart from getting a bollocking – sorry – for taking so long...but it was a nice cup of tea."

I'd hoped to have had longer to chat with her, but a large box of delicious-smelling food arrived.

"Eight fish and chips, four portions of peas, one pudding and chips, cheese and onion pie and six buttered flour cakes. £8.80 please."

"Looks like you're feeding an army."

"Well maybe I am – it's our Labour Party branch. Election campaign meeting. We sometimes finish with a fish and chip supper round at my place. You should join us, we need a few more young faces."

"Thanks for the invitation, but I'm in the CP. We're fighting the same battle though."

"Maybe I'll convert you," she grinned, walking out of the door.

Yes, maybe you could, I thought, though I wasn't thinking of political affiliation. My fish, chips and peas arrived and I headed for home at a fast pace, thoughts alternating between the beguiling Midge and those chips.

The opportunity to see Midge again came sooner than I expected. It was a Saturday morning and I'd popped out to buy the weekend *Guardian* and have a leisurely time catching up on the news. Out of dedication and party loyalty I got *The Morning Star* as well, which most days you could read from cover to cover in five minutes.

The flat door bell rang. Unusual, I seldom got unexpected visitors. I opened the door to find Midge sporting a red rosette with a shoal of leaflets.

"Good morning sir, can I ask who you'll be....oh, it's the young revolutionary! Hello..."

"Hello comrade, an unexpected pleasure...."

"Well don't take it too personally, I'm doing every door on Lee Lane. I'm standing for the local elections..."

"Well our party's instructions are to support the Labour candidate, so you've got my vote. Could I offer you a fraternal brew?"

"OK, why not? But can't take too long, I've got three hundred leaflets to deliver and all of Lee Lane to canvass."

There was only one place to sit, in comfort, and that was on the two-seater settee, so it leant a sort of forced intimacy to the situation. I got the tea, with biscuits, and sat down beside her. She was wearing a delicious perfume, a sort of delicate musk. Same lipstick and make-up, but less formally dressed than in the typing room. Slacks and tweed jacket giving her a slightly 'country' air.

"So do you think you'll get in?" I asked.

"No, not this time. This a Tory ward, Horwich South, has been since time immemorial. We've got long-standing Labour councillors in the other ward, which includes the council estates and railway houses. This one is more middle class and Tory."

"So you're saying I've moved up into the ranks of the bourgeoisie in my modest little flat?"

"No, don't be daft, there's pockets of Labour support round here, and you'd be surprised at some of the poverty. But poor people don't vote. Anyway, comrade, I've work to get done. Thanks for the brew."

"So soon?" I asked myself, not wanting her to go.

"Well, good luck..." I ventured a kiss, on the cheek.

She moved her cheek away, to offer her lips. It was more than a comradely peck.

"If you gave all your constituents a kiss like that, victory would be guaranteed," I suggested.

"Mmm, not sure what came over me then. I don't go round smooching every potential voter y'know."

"Well, can this potential voter invite you round for a meal sometime soon?"

"It's a long time since any young man – or old one for that matter – has invited me out so I'm not going to say 'no'. But let me get this election out o'th'road first."

"OK, you're on."

Midge's assessment of her electoral chances proved accurate. She lost to the Tory but increased the Labour vote by a few hundred. Not bad going. What I didn't have was her address to send the invitation to.

I dropped off a 'well done' card at the Works' office reception, with the invitation to come round to mine at 7.00 next Thursday for a meal, if she was available. I got a hand-written note the day after saying "see you next Thursday, but come to mine – 28 Stephenson Street. More room - Midge."

Stephenson Street was one of the series of anonymous railway terraces built by the Lancashire and Yorkshire Railway in the 1880s, named after that most famous of railway engineers.

I got to the house and could see a light in the downstairs room. I rang the bell.

"Hello, come in!" she said, as the door opened. "Thought you might not come."

"Been looking forward to seeing you, and I've brought this bottle of wine...hope it's OK. Blue Nun. Horwich's finest – well, pretty much the only option really."

"That's lovely, though I don't drink much. Th'kettle's boiling if you want a cup of tea first?"

"Thanks, but I wouldn't mind a glass of wine to be honest."

We opened the bottle and Midge produced a couple of wine glasses.

"My Billy – late husband – never drank wine in his life. But he made up for it with beer. Cheers!"

"Cheers!....and congratulations on a good result in the election. Keep at it and you'll get in next time."

"Not sure I want to. I'm on the town council and that can be interesting if you like local nitty-gritty issues. It isn't 'party political' at all, I get on OK with all of them, including the Tories. But going onto Bolton Council would be different. And me and the Labour Group leadership don't always see eye to eye. They regard me as a dangerous lefty. Which is a bit of a joke, I'm just an old-fashioned socialist. I think Michael Foot's a good man and it would be great to have him as leader instead of Callaghan."

"Well we can both agree on that, but I want to see more radical change than what Labour can offer."

"But not like Russia, surely?"

"Christ, no. There's a big change going on within the communist movement – here in Britain, France, Spain and Italy. It's caused a lot of division, between the old-timers who think Stalin was a decent guy and the younger end, 'Eurocommunists'."

"So you lot are as divided as we are in the Labour Party, then? It tires me out these divisions, I'd rather just get on with sorting out practical local issues and leave the theorising to someone else," she said, as she headed for the kitchen.

She'd set up the table in the small living room. Check-printed table cloth with some Doulton tableware, which I recognised from my parents' house when I was a kid.

"I've made chilli con carné if that's OK? Billy was a 'meat and two veg' man, but I thought it'd be nice to try something different. There's some rice as well."

I'd had chilli when I was at Lancaster, but Midge's was a lot better than my student cooking. The Blue Nun didn't exactly sit perfectly with it; I'd been taught enough about wine to realise I should have got a red. But what the hell. We finished the bottle between us and I helped her take the plates into the kitchen.

"You don't need to do that, sit down!" she ordered. I used to say to Billy, there's a red line across that door into the kitchen. Don't cross it. I'm in charge here. Bit of a joke really as he never had the slightest intention of doing owt in th'kitchen."

After a few minutes she came back in and we settled down onto the settee. I wasn't sure what to do next, but Midge took control of the situation by pulling me to her. I got another instalment of that luscious kiss she'd planted on me, that Saturday morning a couple of weeks ago.

My hands stroked her. She unbuttoned the top of my jeans and unzipped me. She knew what to do. But it didn't have the desired result.

"What's up, love, don't you want me?"

"No, Midge, I do...but I'm a bag of nerves. Give me a few minutes."

"OK, don't worry – it happens with a lot of men, not that I've known hundreds. Come on, let's go upstairs."

The bedroom was functional but cosy. The electric fire was on and the curtains were closed. I assumed the picture of the couple on the chest of drawers was her and Billy. She noticed me looking at it and turned the picture round, before pulling me onto the bed.

"That was my Billy. Wouldn't want him watching."

I took off my remaining clothes and lay with her on the bed. "Let's get under the sheets, and turn that bloody light off will you?" She asked. "You'll feel more relaxed." I did as I was told and got under the bedclothes.

"Just cuddle me for a minute will you love, there's no rush?" she asked.

I gradually started to revive. I was enjoying the feel of this woman's body.

"You're a lovely lad, y'know....I hope you aren't put off because I'm old enough to be your mum?

"Give over...you're beautiful."

I suppose you'd like to know what we did. Part of me feels a certain reticence. Billy Wrightson must have been a bloody lucky bloke, that's all I can say.

"You're not bad at this are you, once you get going?" she asked. "What happened to that shyness?"

We lay, arms around each other, for at least twenty minutes, occasionally looking at the picture of Billy, with his back turned to us.

"So, shall I make a cup of tea then?"

6

Midge

I was happy but slightly conflicted. I was thinking that things with Judy might have developed a bit further. Sure enough, the next few days I saw more of her and we had some nice times. It was a hot summer and we spent balmy evenings lying in the heather on the moors above Horwich, though we never got beyond a bit of fondling and kissing. We both knew it couldn't last. She was going back to university and she'd have other men to distract her who'd have better prospects than a footloose commie working in the Smithy. But there was Midge. After my first evening at her place I was hoping for an excuse to see her again.

It was the following week. I'd been doing a bit of overtime and was leaving the Works heading for home on my bike when I saw her walking back from the shop with one of her mates. I pulled in and said hello.

"Oh it's the young lad," said Midge. "Janice, I'll catch you up in a bit, alright love?" Janice gave her mate a wink and carried on down the street.

"What have you been up to then?" she asked.

"Oh not much, we've got a big job on so I'm doing overtime most days."

"Oh yes, not what I've heard. You seem to have managed to do a bit of overtime with that lass of George Aspinall's."

As I've said, I'm an unconvincing liar so I seldom bother trying. I could hardly deny it. "Well yes, we're good friends but she's off back to Bristol University next week so I won't be seeing much of her for a bit."

"So I suppose you'll be looking for something else to keep you from being bored?"

"I'd not forgotten you Midge. It's just, well, I've been a bit busy, y'know."

"Aye lad, I do. And I don't blame you. I'm just enjoying making you squirm a bit. Do you want to pop round for another cup of tea then, perhaps after your young bird has flown south?"

"Well yes, I would. And I was going to ask you anyway. Really."

"Come round next Wednesday then if you're not doing anything more interesting."

I bent over from the bike to give her a kiss but she pulled away from me. "I'm a respectable widow think on - I don't like being seen kissing young men in the street, thanks very much."

Next Wednesday took ages to arrive. I'd thought a lot about her, and Judy. How I could have ended up being involved with two women so totally different was a puzzle. Judy was politically right-on, academic, middle class. She'd certainly lost most of her accent; Bolton School had cured her of that. Midge was the opposite. Left school at 15, got pregnant soon after, married at 16 and spent most of her married life at home bringing up kids. She ended up with four of them.

Our evening together gave me a chance to get to know more about her, this time over home-made steak and kidney pie, and another bottle of Blue Nun which I supplied.

Midge told me that after Billy was killed she decided to go out to work. She got a good pay out from BR for her husband's death – the union had fought hard for a compensation deal – but she really wanted a bit of companionship. She did a typing course at the local tech and started at the Works offices as a CO1 typist – bottom of the scale, but she didn't mind. And she already had lots of mates in the offices and typing pool.

By the time I'd met her, all the kids had left home – the eldest, Jackie, had got in at university to do English and her brother Joe had won an apprenticeship in the Works and was now a boilersmith. Sarah had got married; Michael had turned into some sort of hippie and gone 'travelling'.

Midge gradually evolved from being a housewife who cooked, cleaned and opened her legs to Billy's willy every Friday evening, to becoming an independent-minded 40 something. She'd retained her good looks despite the four kids - and there was no shortage of blokes at the Works who would have liked to try it on.

Those that did try generally got short shrift. The incident with Joe Harkness became legend. He was one of the more obnoxious personnel officers. He suggested that performing some 'extra duties' not listed in her job description could lead to her rapid promotion. She told him she was happy enough with her current duties, thanks all the same. It happened one Friday afternoon, after he'd got back from having a few pints in the club for a retirement. He followed Midge into the store room and she felt his hands going round her breast.

"Come on Midge, just a little kiss..."

Instead of a kiss he got a punch that would have done credit to one of the strikers in the Smithy.

"I could get you sacked for that, you bitch!"

"Just you fucking well try, and don't try it on with any of these younger lasses either you shit, or we'll have you. It's not my fault you walked into that shelf – and there aren't any other witnesses."

Works Offices

Midge was sure of her ground. Like most of the other women, they were in the union and they'd got a good full-time officer, Amanda Chorley, covering the Works. Midge and a couple of the other women in the offices had attended a weekend school on women's rights and she'd liked what she heard.

"We've put up with being groped, insulted and humiliated for too long," Amanda told them. "We're not going to accept it any more. Sexual harassment isn't trivial, it's a serious issue and if it happens to you, report it. Stand up for your rights!" Amanda didn't say 'lay out the bastard who was doing it' but this was Horwich Loco Works, not academia.

The women were in a different union to us. The 'wages grades', mostly the blokes, were in either the railwaymen's union – NUR ('no use rushing') or one of the engineering unions, whilst the clerical grades were in TSSA – Transport Salaried Staffs Association - which is still waiting for an amusing acronym.

Midge attended the branch meetings and became treasurer. She was good with money and enjoyed the book-keeping, which most other branch activists hated. She went to union conferences, met other activists. People like her – they'd not been to university, most of the women had fought their way out of domesticity, had started to think. About the world they were in, about politics, history, economics, philosophy. Amanda took a shine to her and suggested she should see about doing a degree.

"Me? Give over Mandy. Look, it's nice of you to suggest it, I'm flattered, but I'm quite happy here in Horwich with my mates, doing the union stuff, spending Saturday nights getting pissed in Bolton and flirting with blokes in The Prince Bill. I'd be out of my depth at any university."

Amanda could see her point; the world of a middle-aged working class woman from the North of England was a million miles away from Oxford, Cambridge or any other university. But she read. Her daughter Jackie started suggesting novels, some feminist stuff as well.

"Feminist? I'm not a bloody feminist Jackie, going round burning my bra and all that. I need my bra!"

"Mum, listen - that isn't what feminism is about, that's the sort of stupid patronising crap you get in the papers. Feminism is about women taking control of their lives, being independent and equal with men. You're already a bloody feminist, whether you know it or not! We all know what you did to that bastard in the office."

"Oh I don't know, let's have a look anyway. What have you brought me this time?"

"Well, have a look at these – Germaine Greer's *The Female Eunuch* and this one - Marilyn French's *The Women's Room*. It's only just come out and it's a brilliant novel, you'll like it.

Things progressed with Midge as contact with Judy became less frequent, separated by time, space and perhaps class. The letter arrived in November.

Dear Dave,

Hope you're keeping well. I've something to tell you, and I hope you won't be hurt. I've been seeing quite a lot of Paul, a guy who is on the same course as me. We've decided to share a flat together. I've not told mum and dad, they might be a bit shocked. But thanks for the nice times we had, look after yourself. – Love, Judy"

At first I was well pissed off. Wounded pride. Found someone more 'suitable' I convinced myself. But at least it made my life easier, avoiding any complications with Midge. So fair enough. I could tell her me and Judy had decided to call it quits and that was that.

7

February 1979:   On strike

The strike started in late February. The unions had put in a claim for a 5% across-the-board increase for the railway workshops, after years of wages slipping behind the rest of the engineering industry. The company – everyone still called it that, 30 years after nationalisation - offered 2%, with strings. 'Changed working practices' management suggested, shorthand for job cuts, speed-up and expecting a lot more for less. Stuff that. Places like ours were still being kept going with outdated equipment, some of it stretching back to the nineteenth century. If BR had invested in new equipment, they'd have got their productivity gains. It felt like they wanted a strike as an excuse to shut more workshops down, like they'd done with Gorton, Darlington and Shildon.

The unions held a ballot on the management offer, recommending rejection. On a high turnout, about 85% threw out the offer and were prepared to strike for a better deal.

I'd never been on strike before. It was a myth that the railways were forever out on strike; if anything our union leadership was far too moderate, in bed with the management. Our regional officer, Bert Blackburn, had started off as a left-wing firebrand up in cast Lancashire but had settled into a cosy life as a red-baiting right winger who loved attending expensive dinners at company expense, with his 'good lady wife' as he called her.

There was a story that at some dinner with the bosses a clever arse got an expensive bottle of wine, drained it – probably drank the stuff – then refilled it with Vimto. It was passed round to Bert and his cronies. "What do you think of the wine, Bert?" he was asked. "Mmm, very nice...quite sweet to the palate but yes, most delightful." What a plonker.

I had got involved in the union and became vice-chairman of the local branch. Unlike the leadership, we were quite a left-wing branch and that didn't go down well with Bert, nor with the national executive. Some us were in 'the Party' whilst probably the majority were Labour men, but sound. I suspect the national leadership would have been more keen than the bosses to see the Works closed down, to get us trouble-makers out of the way.

We each received letters from the unions saying the strike would begin on February 18th and would be' indefinite'. We knew the leaders had been dragged kicking and screaming into the strike. The papers were already full of crap about 'militants' on the railways holding the country to ransom. Quite how stopping production of recycled wagon springs would achieve that objective we weren't sure. To have any impact on the railways' operation it would need a long drawn-out strike with trains having to be cancelled because they didn't have the rolling stock. If the unions had brought out the signalmen and drivers that would have had an immediate impact but we were split. "Why should we lose money for the shopmen?" I heard one NUR signalman arguing in the club. "They never supported us when we were out."

Oh yeah. When was that? 1926?

Erecting Shop

Union membership at the Works was virtually 100%. Back then there was a compulsory membership deal with British Rail Engineering. The only exceptions were members of the Plymouth Brethren, whoever they were. If you want my opinion, those sort of deals with management weren't such a good thing. It made the unions lazy and too keen to take the management side. Why worry about standing up for the membership if everyone had to be in the union anyway?

The branch committee met in 'emergency session' as our chairman pompously called it. Back room of the Railwaymen's Club, with drinks paid out of branch funds.

"Well brothers," Arnold Ollerenhsaw, intoned. "We face a decisive battle with management which we can't afford to lose. We've got to see the strike through to victory and play our part here at Horwich. I propose that we mount a 24-hour picket on the Works gate and bring all activity to a standstill."

I sat in open-mouthed astonishment. What did they hope to stop? No real work would get done. The office staff would carry on coming in – the TSSA nationally voted not to strike, surprise surprise – though it was narrower than some expected. A picket would be laughed at; the only work we'd stop would be typing a few letters and delaying orders for equipment. Yet here was our chairman expecting us to stand outside the gate on a freezing February night just to fly the union flag. He could piss off. Fortunately common sense prevailed.

"Could I amend Brother Ollerenshaw's suggestion to a day-time token picket, thus ensuring that no back-sliders slipped through - and we can show we're doing our bit?" I proposed.

It was seconded, put to the vote and carried unanimously. The strike would begin next Monday and a token force of half a dozen of us would picket the main gate. Before work finished on Saturday lunch-time we dragged a couple of braziers out of the Boiler Shop and placed them by the gate, next to the time-keeper's lodge. The three guys who staffed it were all 'green card' men who'd worked on the shop floor and been invalided out. Two were stone deaf, one had lung disease. They still carried union cards but we decided to make an exception of them and not bring them out. We wanted access to their brewing facilities, for one thing, while we were on picket duty.

We got down to the gates on Monday morning at 6.30 with our union banner, a stack of leaflets explaining our claim, and a few placards. It was bloody freezing with a hoar frost on the bushes outside the office block; you could make out patches of snow on Rivington Pike.

We made up a banner to put alongside the fence aimed at passing cars. "Honk if you support us" it said.

The first few cars that went past did give the occasional honk, though one driver - arsehole - wound down the window and shouted at us to 'fuck off back to Russia'. Most passed in silence. Not an auspicious start, but by 8.00 the office staff were starting to arrive, giving us something to do.

"Come on girls, support us and come out on strike!"

"Oh yeah, maybe we'll have our own strike and stop cooking your bloody teas. And more." replied Mildred Basset, one of the more vocal ladies from the admin office. "You'll be wanting our wage packets after a few weeks on strike, won't you?"

Kitchen in the Canteen

Which was true for a lot of the blokes. I wasn't in that fortunate position of having a wife or girlfriend who could see me through, though I was rather hoping that Midge would make me the occasional tea, real as well as metaphorical. I saw her walking down towards the gate.

"Well, the revolution's started then, has it?" she said to me.

"Very funny, but you're the big trade unionist now, Midge, going off to all these conferences, why aren't you coming out with us?"

"Most of us in the typing pool voted to strike, as it happens. It went against us nationally and we were instructed to stay at work and 'not undertake any work done by our shopmen brothers' as the union circular told us. So you'll be relieved to know that we're not going down to the Smithy to start lifting red-hot wagon springs, much as we'd love to."

"So why not pop up to the picket line during your lunch-break, if your Mrs Watson will allow you, and have a bit of a sisterly chat?"

"She'd see that as fraternising with the enemy," but then whispered "come round tomorrow night if you're not too busy..." and skipped off up the office steps, looking round to blow a sexy kiss in our general direction.

"So what's going on wi' you an' Midge Wrightson then? Are you shaggin' her or what?" One of my fellow pickets, Bernard Nolan, delicately enquired.

"We're just good comrades Bernard, brother and sister united – TSSA and NUR. She's a respectable widow, as you know."

We'd only been out for a week but we were getting bored. The money hadn't run out yet and we started getting 'strike pay' – a measly pittance – from the union. Some of the women from the offices, including Midge, brought us cakes they'd baked specially, which boosted our morale, and waistlines. After a few days away from the Smithy or Foundry, we were already starting to get a bit flabby.

Some of the local shop-keepers were on our side. We got free meat pies, pasties, sandwiches and cups of tea delivered to the picket line. Every Friday the local chippy owner sent his wife round with a box full of fish and chips and cartons of mushy peas. They were wrapped in copies of *The Bolton Evening News*, ironically featuring a speech by the local Tory MP denouncing us as 'Trotskyist wreckers'.

We'd just finished our fish and chips on the third week of the strike when a minibus pulled up outside the gates and about a dozen lads – and a couple of girls – got out with leaflets and copies of *Socialist Worker*. "We've come down from Lancaster University to declare our solidarity and offer you our uncritical support," one of them said, in a plummy southern accent. "We've brought our special railway strike issue of *Socialist Worker*, available for just 20p."

"Well thanks. Can we offer you a brew as payment in kind?"

It's unfair to say they were parodies of lefty student activists. I got chatting with some of them - mostly sons and daughters of manual workers who – like me – had got into university. There was one guy who looked familiar.

"It's Simon isn't it?"

"Dave!"

I'd known Simon at university. I was in my second year and he had just started. He quickly got involved in far-left politics and was also a member of the Gay Liberation Front, which had a lot of support at Lancaster back then. We'd had a couple of encounters – nothing too raunchy - after meetings of the Socialist Society and I have to admit he was a nice looking lad. But the attractions of the women comrades proved stronger, and my adventures in burning the candle at both ends were short lived. I didn't have much luck at either end to be honest.

We got chatting and he told me he was now doing an MA in Labour History, with bits of part-time teaching with the Workers Educational Association. "I'm living with Michael in a flat in Lancaster. He's an SWP comrade too and would have been here but for having a bit of a cold."

"Poor little love," I teased.

"Now less of that homophobic patter Dave, you don't have to act a complete twat just because you're now one of the horny-handed sons of toil...though I seem to remember you were quite horny when you were doing Sociology at our bourgeois academic institution."

Our university friends stayed with us for a couple of hours but you could see they were starting to get bored. Couldn't blame them, they sold just one paper, more out of pity than political zeal, and their efforts to persuade us to come to a meeting they were holding about 'the need for a general strike' fell on deaf ears.

"Keep up the struggle comrades," said the one with the posh accent, as they boarded their battle bus. "We need to call in and declare our solidarity with the oppressed tripe dressers of Preston and South Ribble on our way back to Lancaster, so can't hang around."

He didn't really say that, but anyone feeling vaguely pissed off and wanting a day or two on strike would have gained their unflinching support.

The bus departed and Simon was still there, chatting with one of the lads on the picket line.

"You don't miss a chance do you Simon? That lad you're chatting to is strictly hetero and living with a hard-faced lass from Hindley who'd have your balls under the Big Hammer if you so much as looked at her bloke."

"Pity, but thanks for the advice. What are you doing tonight? You don't have a spare bed for the night by any chance do you? I was thinking of staying over then going to see some comrades in Manchester tomorrow."

"As it happens I'm not doing anything but open to offers of a bite to eat. I'm fed up with living off pies and pasties every day and I've had to cut down on the ale as well since the pay packet stopped. You can sleep on the floor, I've a sleeping bag you can use."

We had a curry at the Star of India in Bolton, washed down by a few pints of Thwaites' in The Swan on Bradshawgate, Bolton's seedy high street.

I remembered how much I'd liked Simon, even though we'd not kept in touch. He had a playful side to him and didn't take his Trotskyism too seriously. His dad had was a miner in the Durham coalfield before dying of lung disease. Simon spent a lot of his spare time looking after his mum, who'd moved down to Lancaster, while his partner Michael worked in the local hospital.

We rolled out of The Swan just in time to catch the last bus back to Horwich. The driver was a maniac, probably having spent his break in The Griffin and keen to get back in time for a last one. We pissed ourselves laughing as a couple of the old blokes – alecans whom I recognised from the Works - fell out of their seats as he took a corner particularly fast. I rang the bell for my stop.

"The flat's just up here, come on. It's not much, but it's..."

"Home," rejoined Simon. "It's OK, don't knock it."

He produced a bottle of cheap Australian red which he'd bought earlier in the evening. By the time we'd polished off the kangarouge we were completely gone.

It was almost inevitable that we'd end up in bed together. I told myself it seemed unfair to have him sleeping on the hard floor, and if we kept to opposite sides of the bed it'd be perfectly OK.

After a few minutes I felt Simon's hand on my leg. "Y'know, you're a very fanciable guy," Simon slurred. "You'd make someone a lovely wife...."

"Shut the fuck up Simon, I'm on picket duty at 6.30."

But I wanted him too. I turned round to face him and pulled him towards me. Kissing a bloke is a strange feeling when you're used to women. It's the stubble. Simon was fairly clean shaven, I have to say, at least around his face. It was my hand that touched him, before he reached for me.

"Are you sure you want this?" Simon whispered.

"No, you're forcing me you evil swine, I'll hate you in the morning."

But then something in me changed, quite suddenly; memories that I'd tried to suppress. Nerves, but not the same as when I was with Midge.

"Simon, listen, can we just hold each other. I don't think I'm up to this."

"Yeah, sure Dave...don't worry. Is it me?"

"No it's not you. Goes back a long time, in my early teens. Some stuff I try to forget about. You don't mind do you?"

"No, course not, come here. Do you want to talk about it?"

"Not now, but some other time. Not a big deal, really."

We slept soundly and happily. The alarm went off at 5.45 and I crept out of bed to make a coffee. Simon was still fast asleep.

I left him a note on the kitchen table.

"Thanks for a lovely night, milk in fridge, Shreddies on table. See you again sometime. Comradely kisses, Dave xx"

I cycled down to the Works, feeling slightly elated, but a bit sad I'd chickened out at the last minute. Well, mixed feelings. I'd talk to Simon next time I had the chance.

8

Going up The Pike

The strike carried on for three weeks. We had a few more visits from the 'comrades' at Lancaster though Simon didn't show up. One of his SWP pals said his partner was ill. Money became tight but I was able to go round to Midge's for my tea, and sometimes stay the night. Apart from the obvious compensations she did a wonderful breakfast. Sausage, fried egg and beans with toast. My bowl of Shreddies didn't compare. And she was only two minutes' walk from the Works entrance and our heroic band of pickets.

"Come on, get agate I've a job to go to," she said slipping into a bit of mill girl talk. "They'll be expecting you on th' picket line bi now."

After being on strike for three weeks and manning a picket line every day, you start to get - frankly - bored shitless. There were no heroic confrontations with busloads of scabs, no pitched battles with the police. It was all very quiet – and dull. Joe Jolly the local copper used to call round to check that no violent revolutions were underway. He'd join us for a brew in front of the brazier we'd installed by the gates. His dad had worked in the Boiler Shop all his life and still propped up the bar in the Railwaymen's Club most nights, even though he was 90. One of the few not to get lung disease through asbestos boiler lagging.

"Tha wants to get a job in th' force," Joe suggested. "Good salary, pension and retire at 60."

"Thanks Joe. But somehow I don't think they'd have me."

"Why ever not? A bright young lad who's fit as a fiddle?"

"I think being a member of the Communist Party might be an obstacle."

"Oh aye, ah see your point lad. Well, ah'd better be gerrin' along."

At the start of the third week I got a message from Midge as she was leaving work on Monday afternoon. "I've a few days' leave owed to me. Fancy a day out on Wednesday?"

"Yeah, you're on. Where are we going?"

"Oh, nowhere special, thought we'd go for a walk up the Pike."

That suited me, because I was skint. Even with free rail travel going to Blackpool or Southport would have ended up spending money, and I didn't want to sponge off Midge too much. "Let's hope it's not snowing then, that'll be great."

I stayed at my bedsit the night before. Midge's daughter Jackie was with her and I'd be in the way. So I got my boots on, caught the bus and was at her door by 9.30.

"I've made some egg sandwiches," she said, ushering me in. Jackie was at the kitchen table and gave me a look that was half disapproving and half slightly lascivious.

"Don't get any ideas about our Jackie or I'll break your bloody legs, alright?" Midge said as we walked up the street.

"For fuck's sake, I hadn't even thought about it," I said, feeling slightly insulted.

"Good, just don't then."

We headed along Chorley New Road, past the Mechanics' Institute and came to the Works gate. "I'm having a day off lads, if that's OK?"

The response from the brothers was predictably sarcastic.

"Is Mrs Wrightson taking you out for a walk then?" Fred Richmond said. "Ah bet she'll have more stamina than thee," Jimmy Hurst added.

"You're just a set of jealous bastards that's all, I'll see you on the picket line tomorrow."

You're fairly soon out of the town and into 70s suburbia. The path up the Pike takes you through the estate where Judy's parents lived. I was careful to suggest a route which avoided passing their gate.

After five minutes of suburban tedium we were through a field stile and out into open country. It was a cold, bright day with flashes of overnight snow capping the Pike ahead. We walked hand in hand – or glove in glove at any rate. Our breath mingled in the freezing air. Hoar frost hung on the trees.

"Do you do much walking then? I asked Midge.

"I used to be out every Sunday with Billy. He was a keen walker, and cyclist. Secretary of the Horwich Ramblers - used to walk 20 miles in a day and think nowt of it. Sometimes I just left him to it, though I could keep up with him when I was a bit younger."

A few of the older party members were still members of Horwich Ramblers and had some tales to tell about the rights of way battles they'd been involved in back in the 30s. Before then, these moors had seen the Winter Hill Mass Trespass in 1896 when thousands of Bolton and

Horwich Loco Works; Rivington Pike in the distance

Horwich workers fought to win back a footpath that had been closed by one of the local landowners.

"And what about you then, do you manage to do much walking in between bedding all these women you've got?" Midge asked.

"You're mis-judging me, honest love. There's only you. And I've always liked walking, can't you see the wear in these boots?"

We carried on climbing, Midge setting the speed rather than me; a demanding pace it was too. "We can stop off at the Barn and have a brew," she said. "It's not far to go now."

The Barn was an ancient farm building dating back to the mists of time. It had been converted into a café by the canny farmer years' ago and was a honeypot for walkers and cyclists at weekends. It opened every day, though a Wednesday in February was predictably quiet. I spotted a couple of faces I recognised sat down at a table – Jim Lee and his wife Penny, from our local party branch. Penny didn't work and Jim was coming up for retirement so what with the strike they had plenty time on their hands. Oddly he wasn't that involved in the union. He'd been down to the picket line with copies of the Morning Star and Penny had baked some nice cakes for us, but that was pretty much it.

"How do lad, and nice to see you Midge," Jim said as we sat down. "Are you off up the Pike?"

"Yes, Midge has taken some leave and we've dropped lucky with the weather. It's cold but you soon get warmed up walking at Midge's pace."

"Aye well Billy were a good walker, weren't he? But hey, I hope y' don't

47

mind me sayin'?"

"Course we don't Jim, it's water under the bridge, you've got to move on," she answered.

We say down with our brews and the conversation soon turned to politics. Jim and Penny were long-standing party members who joined during the war when the Soviet Union - and Joe Stalin - was idolised by everyone. Membership of the local branch had shot up to over a hundred. And the Works was turning out tanks for the front-line. There's a photo in Bolton Museum of a tank leaving the Works with 'Good luck Uncle Joe' chalked on the side.

But Joe and Penny weren't Stalinists like some of the branch members. Penny was mainly involved in CND and the Bolton Peace Group. Jim spent most of his spare time researching local history and had published a few pamphlets on 'Old Horwich'. Both he and his wife were working class intellectuals of a type that was becoming an endangered species.

"Ah'm worried about this Thatcher woman," Jim said. "Labour's doin' badly an' if there was an election the bloody Tories will be back in government, wi' that right-wing bitch in charge."

"Now then Jim", said Penny. "Less o' that, if you don't mind."

"Well you know what I mean. She's evil, and determined to crush the working class. A typical petty-bourgeois, veering on fascist."

"Well Labour's still in with a chance," Midge volunteered. "We've not been doing that well recently with Callaghan in charge, but people won't go for the kind of right-wing Tory Government that she'd represent."

I didn't want to contradict Midge but I feared the worst. "I think Labour has let a lot of people down and they've run out of ideas. It's the right that is coming up with new policies however repugnant. Eric Hobsbawm is right what he said in his article in *Marxism Today*. 'The Forward March of Labour Halted'. And it has. The progress made since 1945 is coming to an end and people are fed up with Labourism. It feels like socialism has run out of steam, apart from a few people in the Labour left and the 'Eurocommunists' in the CP."

"Yes," said Midge, "but how big is your Communist Party? 20,000 members? You get a handful of votes in the local elections – even though people respect men like Jim. But they vote for Jim despite the

'Communist' label. Why don't you join Labour and bring all that enthusiasm into the party, and do some good instead of just being on the fringes all the time?"

"We're too old to change now love," said Penny. "We joined during the war when it was a life and death fight between the Nazis and democracy. The Communists were at the forefront of that, in France, Italy, Greece – and here for that matter. To leave now would be like leaving a family. It's our friends, people we've grown up with. And we can still influence Labour, from the outside, like we're doing with CND."

I could see her point. And I could see the CP slowly dying, as younger people joined the far left, like Simon's SWP. The more realistic - or careerist - ones joined Labour, with the hope of getting on the council, or becoming an MP or a trade union official. Neither was an attractive choice for me. I'd flirted with the far-left at university but never felt comfortable with their idealised notion of 'the workers'. Coming to work at Horwich was a rejection of all that, and joining the Communist Party put the seal on that denial.

"Well anyroad," said Midge, finishing off her mug of tea. "This isn't getting us up the Pike and it might start snowing again this afternoon. Let's get goin'. Very nice to see you Penny, Jim."

"And you too lass, Jim said. "Keep an eye on this lad, won't you?"

"Ah will do – he needs it!"

The path towards the Pike took us through the derelict 'Chinese Gardens' where I'd played as a kid. It was part of the estate that Lord Lever had developed from the profits of his soap empire. I suppose he was one of the better capitalists and I had a grudging respect for what he'd done with the estate, which he left to the public. But I couldn't resist chuckling at the Suffragettes who set fire to his house during the fight for women's votes. The ruins of the huge mansion that he jokingly (or perhaps not) called 'The Bungalow' were still there, a monument to the Suffragettes' determination and bravery. Or maybe desperation; but at least nobody was killed.

The further up towards the Pike we got, the colder – and windier – it became. We found an old ruin of a farmhouse a bit higher up and stopped for one of Midge's sandwiches. There was nowhere to sit down but we found a corner away from the wind. It was still bloody freezing, but the compensation was the view across Lancashire and out to the Irish Sea, and huddling up to Midge. The butties were good too – cheese and piccalilli, followed by Midge's fruit cake. Memories are made of such trivia.

It took us another half an hour to get to the top and we could see some dark clouds coming in from the east. Looking down from the small tower that had been erected back in the 1800s, the view was even more breath-taking.

"Can you see Blackpool Tower over there?" Midge asked. "And look, there's Southport straight ahead, with the gasometer. When you're back at work we can go for a trip one Saturday."

The one thing missing from the scene was the smoke coming from the Works. Even on a Saturday you'd see the yellow smog emerging from the foundry, and many other chimneys from each of the workshops at 'the Loco'. There were still plenty of factory chimneys rising up towards the clouds in Bolton, and northwards to Chorley and, further away, Preston. The cotton mills were getting fewer in number but there were still some operating, though they'd long since stopped using steam power.

My mum had worked at The Bee Hive, one of the bigger mills in Bolton, up until a few years ago, on the charmingly-named 'housewives' shift' in the evening. You'd do your 'day job' as a housewife, feed the kids and get tea ready for the man, then start in the mill at 6.30 for three hours and then come home. And husband probably wanted his matrimonial rights after.

"Come on, stop dreaming, give us a quick kiss and let's get going back down," Midge said, grabbing me round the waist.

"Ouch, wait 'til I get you back to yours..."

"Promises mi lad, let's hurry up then. There's a nice cup of tea waiting....and more if you're lucky."

We headed back towards Horwich and felt the first flakes of snow coming down. It was going dark. I was looking forward to that cup of tea.

The strike ended a few days after our walk up the Pike. The union accepted a 'final offer' of a 2% increase, backdated a few weeks. It hadn't been worth going on strike for but we'd made a stand. I'd enjoyed the first few days of picket duty and it was good to have met up with Simon again, in every respect. We went back to work the following Monday, with a sense that there was unfinished business. Management kept harping on during the strike about the need for more productivity, the impact of falling traffic levels and less need for wagons and locos. Unless you were blind, it was bloody obvious that the writing was on the wall for Horwich Loco Works. It said "you're all fucked".

The 1970s were a bad time for the railways. Sure, the Beeching closures were a thing of the past but what was happening now was death by a thousand cuts. Thatcher had it in for us and investment reduced to a trickle. No new locos were being built and places like ours were reduced to patching up knackered trains and wagons. After the strike, morale was at rock bottom and anyone who could take their redundancy did, or found other jobs. Many railway workshops around the country had already closed. We'd received a lot of blokes made redundant from the wagon works at Earlestown after it closed and other places followed suit – Gorton, Oswestry, Wolverhampton and Darlington amongst many more. It felt like we were living on borrowed time.

Some of the older blokes couldn't wait for the closure notice to be issued. They'd get generous redundancy payments and they could buy that bungalow in Southport they'd always dreamt of, if the asbestosis didn't get them first. Sod the rest of us, with families to bring up.

9

September 1979:   Changes afoot

After the end of the strike life carried on much as normal at the Loco, for the time being. We got some work from the south of England as BR continued closing down 'uneconomic' workshops like Ashford. We were even getting a bit of overtime, though 40 hours a week in that place was usually enough for me. But the extra money came in handy for a plan that was shaping up between us.

By now, we had a Tory Government. Thatcher got elected in May. Horwich and Bolton stayed Labour, but Westhoughton went Tory.

Midge was still involved in the local Labour Party. I'd been nagging her to stand for the Council again, even though she said she'd not bother after that last campaign in Horwich South, when we first met.

"Why don't you give it a go Midge? The Council needs shaking up and you'd be good at it. Everyone in Horwich knows you."

At the branch meeting in September the secretary told the handful of members present that the Bolton District Party was asking for nominations for 'the panel'. This was the panel of candidates who had been approved by the District party as being suitable to go forward for election. One of the branch members, Jean Dutton, proposed Midge.

"Midge would be a brilliant councillor," said Jean. "She increased our vote when she stood last year. We might dislodge more of the Tory vote and get a Labour councillor elected if we put up a strong campaign with a good candidate."

She was unanimously supported and her name went forward. Within a few weeks Midge was invited to attend a meeting of the District Party to be interviewed 'for possible inclusion on the panel of candidates.'

The committee interviewing potential panel members – there were another four from around the district – comprised the district secretary, Brian McIvor, the party chair, Margaret Dolan, with a couple of Labour councillors including Jerry Guignan who had been known as a bit of a firebrand in his younger days. He'd settled down to relative anonymity as chairman of the Housing Committee.

Midge was called in to the interview room.

"Thank you for coming, comrade, please take a seat," offered Brian McIvor. "You've a very good record of local activity and we see that you're active in your union, which is very good. There is one thing that worries some of us, let me be frank."

"Oh yes, what's that then?"

"It's your relationship with David Horrocks, a high-profile member of the Communist Party. If he was to run against Labour, on a Communist party ticket, it would cause considerable embarrassment if you were standing as a Labour candidate."

"Well first of all what me and Dave do is our own business. He's a good socialist and I've tried to talk him in to joining Labour, but he won't have it. But the chances of him standing for the CP are nil; he's far too involved with the union. But if it presents a problem for you, I'll withdraw."

Jerry Guignan was quick to intervene.

"No, don't take it like that Midge. We want you as a Labour candidate. Personally I've no problem with the CP, as long as they don't stand against us and let some Tory in. I worked with communists down the pit and they're decent chaps I know. "

"I agree Jerry," said Margaret Dolan. We need more women councillors and it shouldn't matter who they're sleeping with! We all know that our Leader has been seeing quite a lot of that Tory councillor in Harwood, but nobody has raised any questions about that!"

The reference to Councillor Hutchinson's longstanding affair with one of the Tory Group's more right-wing councillors, Aggie Smith, was common knowledge and the cause of much hilarity amongst both parties.

"Well yes, Jerry and Margaret have valid points. Midge, can we ask you to leave the room while we discuss the issue?"

Midge was only sat outside for a few minutes when she was called back in by the chairman.

"Comrade Wrightson, we are delighted to accept you on to the panel of candidates. We note what you've said and we're happy to accept your assurances that you will act in such a way that would not bring the Labour Party into any disrepute. Which is what we ask of all our candidates."

"Well, thank you comrades. On the basis that what applies to me applies to everyone, I'm willing to come onto the panel."

"We are very pleased that you will," said Jerry. "The next step is to find a suitable vacancy – which might not be until next May when it's council elections. However, if there's a casual vacancy before then, your name will go forward for consideration by the relevant branch, along with other members of the panel."

I met Midge outside the party offices and found her in a foul temper.

"The cheek of that chairman, Brian McIvor! Saying that my relationship with you could cause 'embarrassment' to the bloody Labour Party! I've a good mind to join you lot!"

"So they haven't accepted you then?" I asked.

"Well yes, they have, but it's the way they did it that annoys me!"

"Come on love, let's go and get a drink...."

I had mixed feelings about it all; I knew she'd make a brilliant councillor but the Labour Group was still dominated by the old guard, right-wing Labourites. I couldn't imagine her getting along too well with some of them. Especially the Leader, Hutchinson.

The world was going to change, but despite our political commitments, we had other things on our minds.

I'd been spending more and more time at Midge's place; we were in love. I couldn't bear being away from her and it felt pointless keeping the flat going.

"Midge, listen," I said one night at her house. "How about us living together?"

"Well it had crossed my mind but I thought I'd wait for you to say summat. Are you sure you want to live with an old hag like me?"

"Don't be bloody daft. You're a million times better looking than most lasses half your age. I'm besotted with you."

"Aye, and I am with you Dave, really I am. But feelings can change. I can see you running off with a younger piece in a few years time when you get bored with me."

"Don't talk daft. Midge, listen, I've been thinking about this. I've got a bit of money from my dad that he's saved up. Says it's better being used now than waiting for him to die. Would you sell this place and pool our resources in a cottage up on the moors?"

"On the bloody moors? Don't be ridiculous! This place might be small but it's handy for work and th'shops. I don't want to be trailing miles to get home in th'snow and rain. You do get some funny ideas. But I wouldn't mind something that's not too far from town."

So I put my romantic notions of a windswept moorland cottage aside and we started reading the *Evening News* property pages every week to see if anything popped up. We saw a place for sale in the private ads that sounded good. "2-bedroom cottage for sale, near Horwich Town Centre £4,000. No time wasters." I rang the number during the dinner break and a strong Irish voice answered. "Who's that?" it said.

"Is the house still for sale?" I asked.

"It is. Will ye be coming to see it then?"

"Well yes if that's OK. When would suit you?"

"Come round tonight at 6.30 after I've had me tea, and don't be late because got my darts night. The name's Doherty. Paddy Doherty."

I'd arranged to see Midge outside the typing room and told her the news.

"He sounds a funny old bugger," I said. "Irish."

"Well, we're not after livin' with him. Did he say anything more about the house?"

"Well no, not really. But it's a nice area, so let's see."

The place we were going to see was in an enclave of weavers' cottages, dating back to the 1820s. Unlike the railway houses, built with Accrington brick, these were made of stone and looked the better for it.

We found no. 14 George Street – conspicuous with a hand-written 'For Sale' sign on the window - and knocked on the door.

"Come in, I'm glad to see you're punctual." said Mr Doherty, a thin, wiry old lad, probably in his early 70s. "Will you be having a cup of tea first?"

Never refuse a cup of tea, basic working class courtesy. We sat down on the settee and our tea duly arrived.

"I'm livin' on me own now, since the missus died," Mr Doherty told us. "I'm moving down south to be with the children – they're grown up and doing some fancy jobs in London - and my eldest son Dermot has said I must come and live in his place in St Albans. Since Siobhan passed away the house has got untidy, I can't be bothered with the cleaning, and I'll be well looked after down there."

Our host relaxed and told us to call him 'Paddy'. "Part of me would like to be back home in Ireland, but with all the trouble there – I'm from Derry – the kids won't hear of it. And it's going from bad to worse."

The election of Thatcher and the Tories earlier in the year had raised the stakes, that was certain, and the IRA were waging all-out war against 'The Brits'. I was on their side, but you had to be careful what you said and to whom, in case it caused offence – or worse.

"Well let's hope it gets sorted out," I said, being as diplomatic as I could. "When working people are at each other's throats it never does much good."

"Aye, that's all very well. But I was brought up on The Waterside, which even back then in the 50s was mainly Protestant. We were Catholic and I can tell you it wasn't easy. Some of our neighbours were decent folk but there was a nastiness there. I got out as soon as I could and came over here and got a job in the pits. The rest of my family were forced out in '69 and they got a council house on The Creggan, a Catholic area. But that's history, I can't see an end to it. So much bitterness on both sides and Mrs Thatcher determined to pour oil onto troubled waters. Anyway, you'll be wanting to look round then?"

Paddy showed us the living room, with its stern-looking picture of Christ above the fireplace. It was a decent size, larger than Midge's living room. The kitchen had plenty space too, with enough room to eat in. There were two large bedrooms upstairs and a cellar as well. There was a small bit of garden at the back. "It's a nice wee sun trap out here in summer," our host told us. "The neighbours are friendly folk and you'll not have any trouble."

We looked at each other with those expressions that spoke agreement.

"So, Mr and Mrs...whatever ye are...do you want it then?"

"Yes – we do," chirped in Midge. We love it."

"Right then," said Paddy. He reached over to the window and pulled the 'For Sale' sign away. He reached for his pen and crossed out the lettering replacing it with SOLD.

"That's that then. I suppose you'll be wanting to get a mortgage and all that?"

"Yes, it might take a while, is that OK?"

"Oh yes, I'm in no great hurry, my son's got a big house with plenty of room for his auld da."

We moved in just six weeks later. Mr Doherty had left a hand-written note on the mantel piece. "Enjoy your new home – I've been happy here and I hope you will be too – Paddy."

10

1980:   Politics – and a trip to the Illuminations

Midge's entry into local politics proved a bit of a damp squib at first. As the May elections loomed, Midge was invited to a couple of selection meetings around Bolton but felt she was 'making up the numbers'. She could see the hand of the Council Leader, Jack Hutchinson, in moves to keep her away from 'winnable' wards. In Horwich, the town was divided into two wards which returned three councillors each. Horwich North was solidly Labour, whilst Horwich South was all Tory. The sitting Labour councillors were decent enough guys, diligent ward councillors with no ambitions to be committee chairs, even if they wanted to be. And to get those 'plum' jobs with extra allowances, you had to be well in with the Leader. Midge was happy enough to be selected by the Horwich branch to go forward as Labour candidate for Horwich South again, knowing full well she'd have no chance winning. She got the Labour vote up from 1200 to 1600 but still lost by 500 votes to Jimmy Greenhalgh, a longstanding Tory stalwart and local chip shop properietor, known as 'Chip Butty'.

She shook hands with her opponent at the count and wasn't too crestfallen when the vote was announced.

"Never mind lass," newly-elected Councillor Greenhalgh commiserated. "There's plenty of winnable wards around Bolton if your Leader would give you a chance."

"That's not going to happen Jimmy. But I've plenty to keep me busy."

"Aye, well pop round tomorrow neet for some fish and chips. On the house."

Keeping busy? Midge loved organising; apart from her union work she was secretary of the Works' Office Social Committee, chair of the Works Safety Committee and collector for the local branch of REPTA – the Railway Employees' Privilege Ticket Association. This wasn't a group of ticket-collecting enthusiasts but a BR social network that organised trips all over the place, including Europe, using our travel passes.

One of her less ambitious travel projects was the annual night out to Blackpool to see the illuminations, 'the lights'. Always early October. It was mainly for the lasses from the typing pool, kitchen and admin office but husbands and boyfriends were welcome too, if they could stand the pace.

We arranged to meet up at Bolton station at 5.00pm on a Friday evening. There was a deal with management that we'd be allowed to finish a bit earlier without loss of pay, so we could get changed and smartened up. We'd make the time up the following week. We piled onto the 575 bus and were soon away down Chorley New Road, heading for Bolton. "We're all going to Black...pooool" the girls, already half-pissed from spending a few hours in The Bridge, were crooning. The bus driver was glad to see the back of us when we arrived at the station.

Midge had sorted out a group pass and the train – with a couple of reserved coaches – pulled in on time at 5.15. We piled in and the train set off, coughing and spluttering through the series of short tunnels before we passed the Gasworks and Croal Mill. We were soon out into more open countryside, passing the cemetery where my grandad was buried.

The train gathered speed and after a few minutes we could see the Works in the distance. Some of the girls waved... "See you on Monday, if we have to..." one shouted. "Right, who's got the drinks?"

Midge and her mate Gladys, one of the more senior members of the typing pool, had been delegated to get the drinks organised for the way out. Tequila, sherry and cherry brandy for the girls, bottles of ale for the lads.

"I hope someone remembered the bottle opener," Chris Garside shouted.

"Look, we're organised," Midge shouted back. "We've even got some plastic cups for us more refined ladies, you lot can sup from th'bottle."

It was getting dark by the time we passed Preston. We could see the lights of Blackpool Tower in the distance after passing Kirkham.

"I can remember when I was a girl going on day trips to Blackpool," said Midge as we snuggled up in our seat. "We had a competition for who'd be the first to spot Blackpool Tower. Takes me back..and when I was a teenager we used to have some fun with lads in the old-fashioned carriages that didn't have corridors. I could tell you a few stories to make you jealous."

"Oh, go on then. I'm all ears."

"Cheeky bugger, I've got to have some secrets. But it was all fairly innocent. Snogging, a bit of touching up but nothing too serious. Oh, apart from that trip when I was courting with Billy, when I was 18..."

"And...."

She went into a whisper so the rest of the party, now in full swing, couldn't hear.

"Well, we'd only been seeing each other for a few weeks and we were both living at home. Billy was an apprentice at the Works and I was working in a shop up Lee Lane. We were coming home on an 'illuminations special' to Horwich, before they closed the station down. It was one of those old coaches and there was another couple in as far as Preston. So we just held hands and kissed a bit. And then it went a bit further..... I think that's when Jackie was conceived, in that railway carriage. We'd just time to get dressed as the train pulled into Horwich. Some of the other couples looked as dishevelled as we did. Eh, happy days."

The train slowed down through Poulton-le-Fylde and Blackpool was only minutes away.

The train pulled into Blackpool North and the doors were already opened before we juddered to a stand. The station staff opened the gates and let us all through rather than try to check anyone's ticket. We marched down Talbot Road, arm-in-arm singing "We're all going on a summer holiday..." – even though it was October and bloody freezing. Still, we were at the seaside.

"Right, sisters and brothers," Midge shouted as we came to a stop at the bottom of the street. "The programme is...drinks in Yates's Wine Lodge, then tram to The Pleasure Beach. All those in favour?"

"Yaay" everyone shouted. We piled into Yates's and Midge ordered the round, using the social committee fighting fund to which they'd contributed over the year. "So it's seven cherry B's, a Tequila Sunrise, four barley wines, three Pina Coladas, eight pints of bitter and two mild please!"

Say what you like about Yates's Wine Lodge, they knew how to handle large groups of determined boozers. It was like a military operation. We were served in less than five minutes and it didn't take us much longer to sup up.

"Right, come on you lot, remember that last train back's at 11.30. Let's get down to the tram stop. Come on Vanessa..."

Vanessa, one of the young typists, gulped down the last of her Cherry B and clung on to Jimmy Moss, an apprentice pattern-maker at the Works.

The party rolled out of the pub and headed down to the tram stop just as one appeared in view. "23 to the Pleasure Beach please," Midge instructed the young conductor. We rattled and banged along the promenade, past The Manchester and tired-looking pubs and hotels. Coming the other way were festooned trams made up to look like American steam locomotives, show-boats and Wild West saloons.

Most of the tram's passengers piled out with us at the Pleasure Beach and we headed across the road to the entrance. We agreed we'd disperse and do our own thing before meeting back by the entrance at 9.30. Some of the lads and their girlfriends were off to ride the Big Dipper, others opted for more sedate rides like the Gold Mine or the Ghost Train. I've always liked the River Caves – a cheesy take on world history and 'the white man's burden' but, for fuck's sake, it wasn't a Sociology lecture. I helped Midge into the boat and away we sailed, past the ruins of ancient Egypt, African tribesmen and Inca warriors. Snogging was expected in the River Caves and we maintained the tradition, emerging none the wiser about world history, culture or geography but enjoying the experience all the same. "Right, where now then?" asked Midge. "I fancy the Log Flume!"

"What, you're joking? You get soaked and in this weather we'll never dry out."

"Don't be a wimp Dave, we're doing it."

The Log Flume is a simplified version of the Big Dipper, with water. You get on a pretend 'log' and climb to a great height then whoosh! down through a lake of water. As the warning says, you will get wet, you may get soaked. In fact Midge had brought along a couple of plastic macs which we put over ourselves, clever girl. We set off and climbed slowly up to the top of the ride, which is all part of building the sense of expectation. And then – whoosh…you gather speed, and it feels like you're really shooting along. You hit the water with a smash and the water shoots up and into the train, bringing the speed down. Most of our fellow passengers were soaked but we got away with a modest dampening. Midge was up for a few more rides, so I just went along with her. The Ghost Train, Grand National and a few more besides. It soon got to 9.30.

Most of the rest of the party were already waiting at the entrance when we turned up. Some of them had obviously been on the Log Flume or Water Chute and hadn't been so well prepared, looking cold, wet and bedraggled.

"Right then, tram back to Central Pier and sit-down fish and chips." Midge assumed control again and we fought our way through the queuing cars back to the tram stop. The social dynamics of the group had undergone some noticeable changes. Donna Brooks from typing had taken an all-too obvious liking to Mike Pendlebury from the drawing office and they were clinging to each other like limpets. Joanne Sharrock, previously attached to Colin Smith from finance had switched allegiance to Annie Garside while Colin was coupled up to the previously unattached Gladys Moss from the canteen. Everyone seemed happy and getting steadily more pissed from the bottles that various members of the group had in their bags.

We ended up in Ocean Fisheries, a classic Blackpool fish and chip restaurant with a pungent smell of domestos.

"You know we're closing in half an hour?" one of the staff informed us, as she swabbed the floor. "Don't worry, we're fast eaters. So that'll be…" Midge rattled off the order, mostly the standard fish, chips and peas, bread and butter and tea. A few of the more deviant members of the party went for steak pudding, with one girl – Vanessa, who'd gone veggie – having cheese and onion pie.

Despite the less than welcoming customer service, the fish and chips were bloody good. We'd built up healthy appetites after the booze and walking round the Pleasure Beach.

"We've time for one last drink before the train home," Midge declaimed. "So come on Vanessa, finish those chips and let's get goin'." Vanessa was famous for being a very, very slow eater, as well as a bit of a hippie. She took everything at a pace that was about half the speed of every other member of the human race. "You enjoy food more when you take your time, you need to be grounded and slowwww..." she argued, spreading out one arm to demonstrate the point..

"Aye, you'll feel well grounded if you end up sleeping on Blackpool railway station if we miss that train. Come on, shape...." her mate Kath told her.

We ended up in the pub between the bus station and the railway station. The King's Arms, which once had pretentions of grandeur. It wasn't clear if the bouncers on the door were there to throw you in or chuck you out but we didn't seem to pose a significant threat. "Good evening ladies, gentlemen, hope you're having a pleasant evening."

"Ooh yes thank you," Denise from finance responded as we were hustled through into the lounge. "He looks nice," she whispered to her friend Nicola. "Wouldn't mind taking him down a dark alley..."

Midge ordered a round using what was left of the social 'kitty', with some of the lads chivalrously making up the few quid we needed to pay for all the drinks. "Right boys and girls, here's to a good night out!" Midge announced.

"Cheers" Well done Midge, you've done a great job, we're all pissed as farts and having a wunnnnnnderful time...." Laura from the typing pool rejoined. "And we've got some more booze for the train back!"

There was another party in the bar, even more pissed than we were. Scousers by the sound of their voices. One of them leered over to me, saying "Taking your mum out for the night, eh lad?" Midge looked away, nervously. Trouble was brewing.

"Just go and fuck off arsehole, piss off back to Liverpool where they might appreciate your crap sense of humour." I shouldn't have been so aggressive, I know, I know. It was the drink and feeling protective of Midge. Mr Scouser didn't appreciate my response and he took a swing at me which fortunately missed. He fell over and Midge accidentally poured the remains of my pint over his head.

One of the bouncers had arrived on the scene by now.

"Is this gentleman bothering you madam?" he asked her.

"Well he didn't mean any harm, he just needs to sober up." He was dragged away, back to his mates who thought the whole episode hilarious.

"Sorry mate, he didn't mean to give offence, he's just a twat when he's pissed," one of his mates said to me, shaking my hand. Decorum was re-established and our new-found Liverpudlian friends and ourselves raised glasses in Lancashire solidarity.

Our departure for the train co-incided perfectly with the landlord calling time. We trooped down to the station and they were just opening the gates to let the seething horde of drunken revellers onto the train. It was a long train of eight or nine coaches hauled by an ageing diesel loco that BR had pressed into service for the illuminations traffic. We had a coach reserved and we piled in, to the sound of clinking bottles. This time we dispensed with the plastic glasses and just drank from the bottle. I slumped down on a seat with Midge and pulled her to me, enjoying the smell of her perfume mixed with beer and fish and chips.

"You want to control that temper of yours, y'know."

"Well, he was way out of order, even his mates knew that. And I was defending you."

"I don't need defending, thank you my knight in shining friggin' armour. I can defend myself. And yes, he was out of order but he was also a bloody sight bigger than you and if he wasn't so pissed he could have flattened you. Never go into a battle that you're not sure you can win."

"Thank you comrade Lenin, always the great tactician" I replied before kissing her on the mouth.

The train was on its way and everyone was in good, intoxicated, form. Hidden bottles of ale and even some wine appeared and communal hymn singing included drunken renditions of 'In The Navy', 'Knock on Wood' (complete with sound effects), and 'Hit Me With Your Rhythm Stick'. Many of the members of the party who had hardly been acquainted previously were draped across each other in passionate embraces. Some of them had husbands and wives to go home to. Most would have little recollection of their goings-on tomorrow.

And thank Christ tomorrow was Saturday.

We were first stop Preston, then Leyland, Chorley, Adlington and Blackrod before Bolton. A few of us got off at Blackrod and walked back to Horwich, most stayed on to Bolton where Midge had arranged a bus to take us home.

So far so good, no-one had been sick. The winning streak came to an end just as we were passing Lostock Junction, nearly at Bolton. "Ohhh, I'm feeling ill." It was Vanessa. It had taken her all the way from Blackpool, just before we were getting off, to decide to be sick. We pulled one of the carriage windows down and let her throw up along the side of the carriage, rather than in the train itself. She sat down looking white as a sheet. "Ohh, I feel terrible...." and then threw up inside the carriage, just missing my leg. "I'm so sorry, so sorry, I just want to go home."

"Don't worry love, we'll soon have you home, we're nearly there..."

We rolled off the train at Bolton and climbed the stairs to find our 'charabanc' waiting outside, the driver looking worried in expectation of another crowd of pissed-up revellers messing up his nice bus.

"Hello Mr Khan, thanks for waiting for us," Midge said, assuringly. "We've all had a lovely time and we're probably a bit tipsy but we'll not mess up your nice bus, promise," she slurred. "My chap here, David, will make sure everyone behaves, won't you David?" raising her voice several decibels before slumping into the front seat, pulling me down with her.

The coach dropped us off at the end of the street and we meandered back to our new home. We fell onto the bed, fully clothed, and went fast asleep.

11

May 1981:   Dad dies; Midge gets elected

The phone rang at about 6.30 - a.m. I was just getting out of bed ready to cycle down to the Works, for a stewards' meeting. It was my brother, Joe.

"Hello Dave. Listen, sorry to bother you at this time. It's your dad. He had a heart attack last night; he's in Townley's. I couldn't get hold of you last night, couldn't find your number..."

Which was fair enough I suppose. Joe and I weren't close. A bit older than me, we'd never had much to do with each other since I left home to go to uni. He still lived in Farnworth and ran a small garage. Dad helped him out from time to time.

"Yeah, OK, I'll get down there now, which ward is he in?"

I rang the Works Office and said I'd be back in later that afternoon.

I jumped on a bus into town then another up to the hospital, what used to be the old workhouse. A forbidding place, only slightly relieved by the children's paintings along the corridors.

I got to the ward at about 8.00 and Joe was sat reading *The Sun*.

He gave me a hug, probably the closest we'd ever been to any sort of physical intimacy for years. If ever.

"It's not looking good Dave. He had a massive heart attack last night while he was working underneath the car."

We got a cup of tea out of the machine; it tasted awful but it gave us a bit of something to do, and moan about. We talked awkwardly about politics – Joe was a bit of a Thatcherite – and the state of the motor trade, about which I knew nothing and cared less.

"How are things going at the Loco Works Dave?" Joe asked. "Dad said you were big in the union now. You always were a lefty, weren't you?"

"Yeah, well I'm senior shop steward for the Foundry and Smithy. Means I don't do much real work, which can't be bad. And it's regular days, apart from the odd evening meeting."

"But don't you think they've too much power? I'm not talking about moderate unions like the railwaymen, but the likes of the miners and car workers. They're always on strike. I know it sounds corny but they're holding the country to ransom."

"It's never so simple. Usually with a strike there's an underlying grievance, often compounded by lousy management. People don't like going on strike and no good union man would be forever getting his members to down tools. When we were out in '79 I'd be first to admit that we didn't gain much. But if we hadn't have walked out we'd have just seen our pay decline even further. It was about running to stand still. But our biggest worry is whether we'll have any jobs to go to."

"Yeah, I've heard there's talk of closing the Works," said Joe.

"More than talk, we're getting ready for the bad news. But we won't take it lying down."

"Well you can't stand in the way of progress. People are buying cars because trains and buses are unreliable and expensive. I could do you a good deal on a Ford Anglia if you're interested?"

"Well thanks Joe, I'll bear it in mind but for now I'll stick to my bike."

Our discussion on the merits of public transport was cut short by the ward door opening. The nurse's expression said it all.

"Are you the sons of Mr William Horrocks?"

"I'm really very, very sorry to say your father passed away a few minutes ago. We'd done everything we could for him. Would you like to come in and see the body?"

How to react when you see your dad lying there – 'a body' – the life gone out of him? We both cried, our tears compounding each other's. We held each other, again.

I thought of all the times I'd been an absolute shit as a son. Never being the boy he'd wanted, crap at sport, pissing around in left-wing politics, getting a job at the Loco Works when I could have been 'summat in an office'. Not getting round to see him as much as I should, not supporting him when him and mum split up. The catalogue of guilt was endless. At least Joe was running his own business and supporting a nice wife and family, even if he did live in a council house on Harper Green. He was hoping to buy it though.

"Come on Dave, I'll buy you a pint. There's nowt else we can do here. We need to sort things out for the funeral."

The big question was – would mum come? Neither Joe nor I liked her 'fancy man' as we slightly jokingly called him. He was anything but fancy, smelt a bit at times, but if he was good to her, what the fuck did it matter. To be honest I was hoping she wouldn't bring him with her, but we both wanted her there.

He'd said he wanted to be cremated at Overdale, up Chorley New Road. He still had a lot of friends from his days at Walker's and we put the word round the institute so people would know. And a small ad in *The Bolton Evening News*.

We asked family and close friends to gather at his house, we reckoned three cars would be enough. Anyone else could meet at the crematorium for the service.

It was a typical spring Bolton day. Pissing down. We assembled at the house in our black suits and ties and said our last goodbyes before the coffin lid was sealed. Joe was going to sort out the house and contents, there wasn't much worth keeping. Forty years in the limeyard, not much to show for it. A few framed pictures of holidays long gone, one or two ornaments and some trophies from his snooker. It had been home for my first 17 years. The house had a bit of garden at the back which dad had looked after and grown a few spuds as well. There wasn't much light as it was in the shadow of Bee Hive Mill, where mum had worked in the Card Room for a few years before she upped and left.

It was a non-denominational service. Dad wasn't religious, though mum stuck to her Catholic faith. She was stood at the entrance to the crem, alone.

"Hello mum, thanks for coming," I said as she tried to make a smile. We exchanged hugs.

"Of course I'd come. It didn't seem right for Jack to though - he sends his condolences. I know you never really forgave me for leaving your dad but there's two sides to that story. But it's not the time nor place to talk about that now."

The eulogy by the vicar was perfunctory but good enough. Joe had done the briefing.

"William – or Bill to those who knew him well – was a good man; father to Joe and David and a conscientious employee at Walker's Tannery, before it closed down. Bill kept himself to himself but was well respected by his workmates. He was a skilled snooker player and was known for his fine singing voice. He liked to read and was a great lover of his garden. He will be sadly missed by all who knew him."

So that was that. The recording of 'Abide With Me' kicked in as the coffin disappeared into the furnace. A life summed up in five or six lines. I knew what mum was talking about. He was a bastard at times and I saw him hitting her on the rare occasions when he'd come back from the club pissed. He didn't particularly encourage me to 'have a career' though he'd hopes for me ending up as a teacher or some sort of 'collar and tie' job. So I was a disappointment. People often say that we owe everything to our parents, though I'm not sure I do, other than the obvious. If anything I took more after mum than dad, as he commented those years ago when I told about my 'career move' to the Loco Works.

With time-keeping that the railways would envy, we were shuffled out of the chapel in readiness for the next service to commence. We hung around in the drizzle outside, shaking hands with other mourners. Some of dad's mates from the Tannery had come along.

"Bill was a very decent man, David," Eric Withers told me as he grasped my hand, maybe a bit too firmly. "He was well liked in the Tannery and even after he became foreman he was never a 'company man'. He had principles and always made sure his lads were looked after."

A woman whom I didn't recognise came up after Eric had gone back to his mates. Quite small, I'd say in her early 70s. "Hello, you won't know me but I'm Dorothy Nuttall. Dot. I worked in the Limeyard with your dad in the 1950s. I was the only woman amongst 50 men. It was a funny place for a female to be, everyone thought it was a bit strange. But I'd been working in the mill and thought it couldn't be any worse than the Spinning Room and the pay was a bit better. So I was taken on and your dad was told to keep an eye on me. And he did. He was a gentleman. Now and again one of the younger lads tried it on but Bill always told them to behave. So thank you for what he did for me."

I was amazed that any woman had ever worked in the Tannery, apart from in the offices and canteen. And I was proud of what she'd said about dad. He never struck me as a champion of women's rights and was a typical Labour-voting reactionary on lots of things, not least race. So there you go, another myth destroyed.

Joe had organised a spread at The Pack Horse, in town. We spent an hour eating ham and cucumber sandwiches, conversing uneasily. We were not what you'd call a close family. Mum left the gathering as soon as it was decent to do so and I walked down to the station with her to see her off. "Please keep in touch, love," she said as the train drew in. "You know you're always welcome at our place, so don't be a stranger. Well, bye-bye David."

The train drew out and I shed a tear. At the time I didn't really know why, but maybe it was for the end of a family that I'd never really bothered much about.

Midge's half-hearted attempt at a political career appeared to be over. The May elections had come and gone and once again she stood in Horwich South, this time against Olive Donaldson, another old-time Tory who Midge got on well enough with. The following day we decided to treat ourselves to a pub meal in The Millstone, a name that seemed highly appropriate given the deadweight of the local Labour leadership.

We sat down with our drinks – Taylor's Landlord for me and a red wine for Midge – and looked forward to the steak pie and chips.

"I think I'll come off the panel, Dave. I'm not going to get a winnable ward in Horwich and Hutchinson will make sure I don't get selected anywhere else around Bolton. Not that I really want to anyway. My heart's here in Horwich."

"Why be in a rush?" I asked. "It doesn't do you any harm to stay on the panel and if it's not too big a distraction to stand for Horwich South. If you really want to become a councillor, Hutch won't last forever."

"Yes love – oh look, food's coming – I know but I want to get a council seat in Horwich, not Farnworth or Halliwell."

"Well OK, just stay put and see what happens. Pass the gravy, love."

I don't know if I'm psychic or what. But two weeks after our Millstone conversation, at the Horwich branch meeting, Ernie Hayes - one of the Horwich North councillors - announced his intention to stand down and force a by-election in November.

"I'm very sorry to have to do this, comrades, but I'm 76 and my wife Doreen is in very poor health. I can't devote the time to her that I need and be a councillor as well. We've got a very good potential candidate here in Horwich – Midge – and if she was willing to stand for nomination she'd have my support. And it would be good to see Hutchinson's face if she got elected!"

"Well this is a bit of a surprise Ernie," said Midge. "I was just about to come off the panel to be honest. But I would like to represent Horwich if the branch will have me as their candidate."

It was put to the vote at a special meeting and Midge was adopted, unanimously. The only other people putting themselves forward were friends of 'Hutch' from Daubhill branch.

The election took place on Thursday November 12th. We knew it was a safe Labour seat but we didn't take chances. 'We' being the local Labour Party helped out by local CP'ers such as myself and some non-aligned lefties who had got to know Midge through her union activity at the Works.

She upped up her majority by nearly a thousand votes.

"Well congratulations, Councillor Wrightson!"

"Point of order Mr Horrocks, your turn to get the drinks..."

Midge was on the Council, but we knew that she'd be consigned to 'the back benches' as long as Hutchinson was leader. But we soon found plenty of things to keep us both busy, nearer to home.

12

June 1982:   The announcement

The first we heard of it was in *The Bolton Evening News*, Wednesday June 21st 1982, nicely timed just before the start of the two-week holidays. "Horwich Loco Works to close with loss of 1800 jobs."

The union leaders feigned outrage, but they knew it was coming. As for the Works Committee, they'd been kept in the dark, as usual, by union head office.

Tommy Hindley, the Works Convenor, was incandescent. "The fucking bastards, they've been planning this for months, probably years. But we're not going down without a fight."

Tommy had been elected convenor about a year ago. He was a steward in the Wagon Shop and had served his time at the Works as a wheelwright. He was in his late 50s and had done his military service in Aden. He was an amiable guy, easy to get on with, though I didn't, at first, get any sense of his politics. Solid, middle-of-the road Labour I'd have guessed. But talking to him about Aden showed a different side. He was there right at the end of that nasty colonial war and ended up more or less siding with the rebels. He and his mates drove round in a British Army Land Rover sporting the flag of the National Liberation Front, half expecting to get court-martialled. But by then even the officers knew the game was over and the sun was setting, rather quickly, on The British Empire. So who cared? And displaying the NLF flag was a good insurance against getting shot at by the rebels. Maybe that political cunning helped him become an effective union negotiator.

He read *The Morning Star* – or *Daily Worker* as he preferred to call it – but kept his politics to himself. "I've enough on wi' th'union beawt gettin' mixed up i' politics," he told me over a pint after a meeting of the Works Committee. "But mi loyalties are wi' you lot."

The Works Committee called a mass meeting of all members the following day, for 10.00 in the Works yard. All work was to stop, for the duration, offices included. Midge and her TSSA members had as much to lose as we had.

Jobs rally at Horwich

"Brothers and sisters. You've heard the news," Tommy's voice boomed across the yard, amplified by the megaphone he'd borrowed from the Sports Club.

"They've shut Earlestown. They've shut Swindon. Gorton, Darlington, and Shildon - all gone. Now they want to get rid of us. Forget the money they've invested in the Foundry, forget that we need new trains, new wagons, new coaches. They'll build them abroad. And what of Horwich? It'll become a ghost town. Shops'll close. Pubs'll shut. There'll be no money; folk'll leave. Jobs? Down south, maybe. Not up here. This town has got a century of railway building. We've got skills that are the envy of the world. Apprentices from India, Africa...they've come here to learn their trade. I'm old enough to remember the war. We worked 16 hours solid, seven days a week sometimes, building tanks to defeat Hitler. That's forgotten. We've got our own Hitlers, who are doing more damage to our railways than the Luftwaffe ever did. We've had Beeching. We lost our own station here at Horwich. They shut as much as they could. Now they're trying to finish the job. Are we going to let them?"

"No!" the crowd shouted in unison.

"So are we going to feyt 'em?"

"Yes!" was the only possible answer, booming out across the Works yard.

"Brothers and sisters, go back to your benches and desks. The Works Committee is meeting to formulate a strategy. We're not going to do the bosses a favour by striking and shutting our own Works down, doing their dirty work for 'em. We're going to make sure that railway building carries on at Horwich, for this generation, and for the future generations. We owe it to our kids, and to eaur grandchilder."

The Works Committee met in the Mechanics Institute – The RMI - across the road. Around the walls were pictures of the locomotives that the Works had turned out over the years, going back a century. Express passenger engines – the old blokes called them 'Highflyers' and 'Lanky Dreadnoughts', big goods locos, 'Austin 7s' and 'Sea Pigs' - and hundreds of tank locos like the 'radial tanks' that could do everything from pull a fast express to shunting the coal yard. The Works had a distinguished engineering tradition and had produced some of the world's greatest engineers. A picture of Nigel Gresley, designer of 'Mallard' and 'Flying Scotsman', beamed down at us as we ordered our pints. He'd served his time here – along with many more.

It was an enlarged meeting of the Works Committee, involving all the stewards from each shop, and even a couple of TSSA reps from the office, including Midge.

"Good speech Tommy," Denis Murphy, deputy convenor said as he handed him a pint. "It got 'em goin' all right."

"Well mebbe it did but hauf of 'em will be wantin' a good redundancy deal an' nowt else," replied Tommy. "And how we resist this one isn't gooin' t' be easy. Anyroad, let's call the meeting to order."

"Brothers – and sister, howdo Midge - we've known this was coming, though I thought it would be more of a gradual run-down. To shut the whole bloody Works in a matter of months is criminal. We can't blame our own management – they're in the same boat as we are, they'll have nowt to manage and they'll have to move to Crewe or Derby if they want to keep a job. We've got to put up a feyt. So, let's open it up for discussion. How can we save this place?"

An audible groan went round the room when Johnny Faulkner jumped up, the one Trot on the Works Committee, from the Paint Shop. "Comrades, the only thing that will stop this closure is a general strike. We've got to picket every factory in Bolton, Wigan, Preston and Manchester. Bring out the engineers, the miners, mill workers, bring out the car workers at Leyland – and get our own brothers and sisters to stop the trains. That's the only way we'll win."

Rally at the RMI to meet jobs marchers

"Johnny, replied the chairman. "Do you really, really think the AEU, the NUM and all the rest are going to give up even a day's pay for us? Come on lad, use a bit o'sense. We needn't be on our own, but we're not going to get anyone losing money for us. And besides, th' miners and cotton workers are shit scared their own jobs are going. Thatcher is after a showdown. She's pumped up the pay for the police and they'll do whatever she says. She'd love a general strike so she could smash us. Why should we oblige?"

"I'm glad someone's showing a bit o'sense," chirped in Harry Hampson, one of the Wagon Shop stewards who was coming up for retirement. "We're not going to stop this place from shutting down, they've been running it down bit by bit for years. I'll be glad to take the money a couple of years early, if the money's reet. I say we fight for a good pay-off and mek the best of a bad job."

There was a bit of a flurry when Midge stood up to speak. "Mr Chairman – chair – it's all very well Harry saying let's just tek the money. If my Billy were still alive he'd have more feyt in him than that. You can't just think of yourselves, what about the young lads – and girls – who are going to be thrown on the scrapheap? They don't want to be moving to Derby or Doncaster. They've got their families here, the kids are going to local schools. We've been here generations. We've got to fight. But Tommy's right that coming out on strike isn't the answer. We've got to fight politically. We've got to get the MPs on side, but we've got to go much further and get this town united in support. We've got to go down to London and make them listen. And we do need the support of the other unions – there's a Trades Council meeting at the Spinners' Hall in Bolton tonight – let's go and lobby them and get their support. We need to spell it out to everyone in this town, in Bolton, Westhoughton, Chorley...closing Horwich Loco Works will affect you all. Yes, Horwich in particular, but many of our members travel in from further afield. This is a threat to the community, all the community. If we can really make the politicians sit up and listen, we might – just might – get them to make the company change its mind."

The meeting stood up and cheered. I felt tearful, and embarrassingly proud. I could have kissed her – but let's leave that for later, I thought. Tommy caught the feeling of the meeting. "Well, it's tekken a lass fert tell us what needs doin'. This is a political fight and will be won through political means. Let's not do what the bosses and Thatcher is wantin' us to do. Let's be clever and try different tactics."

13

The Trades Council meets

The Works Committee agreed to form an action group, involving other unions in the area, community groups, even some of the more vocal shopkeepers who could see demand for pies plummeting if they closed us down. The local churches were all behind us – the Anglicans, Catholics, Methodists, Baptists and Congregationalists. We even got a message of support from the Spiritualists in town, but they held back from telling us what the future held. Maybe it wasn't good news.

We'd told Brian Spencer, chairman of the Trades Council in Bolton, that we'd be coming mob-handed that night. Midge, as the TSSA rep, had rung him up that afternoon. "Aye Midge, of course you'll be reet welcome, we'll give you lads half an hour on the agenda as a special item."

"Thanks Brian...and by the way, I'm not a 'lad'..."

The Trades Council brought together all the TUC-affiliated unions in the area. It was dominated by the engineers – Brian's union – but had delegates from the railway unions, textile trades, even little outfits for coppersmiths, heating and ventilation, and bank clerks. On an average night they'd get about 60 delegates. Tonight would be different.

It was held in the main assembly room of the Spinners' Hall. In the days when Bolton's cotton industry was the world leader, the spinners were the aristocracy of labour. They could afford to build their Spinners' Hall as a lavish statement of union power and self-confidence. Yet they treated their own fellow workers – the side piecers and little piecers – like slaves, and half of them voted Tory. They'd sooner die than let a woman get anywhere near their jobs. They fought tooth and nail against stopping the half-time system which forced their own kids to go into the mill at the age of 12, working as a little piecer in the morning and going to school for a semblance of education in the afternoon. They brought in a few extra shillings a week, and usually it was their dad, the spinner – or 'minder' – who employed them.

The days of the spinners' supremacy had long gone. Less than half a dozen mills in Bolton were still spinning cotton. The textile unions had merged, and soon were to lose even that identity by going into one or other of the big 'general' unions. The old 'minders' would be spinning in their graves, wondering what on earth the world had come to.

Around the main hall were union emblems and fading photos of past general secretaries. Proud-looking men with gold watch-chains, droopy moustaches and an air of superiority combined with almost visible ill-temper. The polished woodwork survived, but no longer shone as it once did when the spinners held their delegate meetings.

"Brothers and sisters, comrades. Can I bring this meeting to order?" Brian rapped the table with his gavel that had been used by union chairmen for generations. "This Trades Council is facing one of the biggest challenges we've had for years. The proposed – and I stress 'proposed' – closure of Horwich Loco will lead to the loss of 1800 jobs directly, but many more on top of that involved in the supply chain. We're fortunate in having several representatives from the Works, representing the many unions that organise at Horwich. Tom Hindley, chairman of the Works Committee, will address the meeting."

"Thank you Brian, and thank you brothers and sisters for inviting us to your meeting. We've always sent delegates to the Trades Council and supported our comrades involved in disputes across the town in the past. Fire-fighters, miners back in '74, nursery nurses, and many more. This struggle is different. We aren't asking for more money, we're fighting for our survival. For our jobs, for the future of our community. If Horwich Loco Works closes, it'll be the end of dozens of small businesses, everything from the pie shop to the pubs. We're talking about a whole way of life. We've got sporting clubs – our own football and cricket teams. We've an amateur dramatic society. Walking clubs. It'll all die without the Works. It's genocide."

Tom shuffled his notes and continued. "Many of my members have already moved once, sometimes twice, from factories that have closed – Earlestown, Gorton and even as far away as Darlington. We can't carry on like this. You know as well as we did that Thatcher wants to destroy the trades unions. After she's done with the railwaymen, finishing off what Beeching did, she'll turn on someone else – the miners, the printers, or engineers. Brothers and sisters the threat to Horwich Loco Works is short-term thinking at its worst and most vindictive. We need our railways and we need to build engines, carriages and wagons. We've got a century of skill at Horwich, we were once respected all over the world. This country's going to need its railways. The roads are getting jammed, you can't carry on building more and more roads and getting more and more traffic. But by the time our railways revive, as they will – mark my words – we'll have no engineering capacity to build new trains. They'll have to go to Germany, France, maybe even Japan to get their trains. And pay a fortune for it. So, brother chairman, we're asking you and members of this Trades Council to give us your full support. Together we can win."

There was tumultuous applause as Tommy sat down. We all felt proud of him. But did we have a cat in hell's chance of winning? My heart hoped we had but my head said no we hadn't a chance. Or, as Gramsci wisely put it – optimism of the will, but pessimism of the intellect.

After the applause died down, Brian asked for questions from the floor.

"Brother chairman," boomed Harry Nightingale from the electricians' union. "We're all behind the Horwich lads. Anyone living in Horwich either has someone in their family working there or knows two or three people that do. The question for Brother Hindley is, 'what help you want from us?'"

"May I, brother chairman?" Tommy stood up again and addressed the room.

"Nobody is saying this fight is going to be easy. BR is determined to shut us down and transfer production to Crewe and Derby. The Government couldn't care less and wants the unions to be hammered. So we've got to fight a major political battle, getting MPs on our side, the press and even the business community. This will affect them as much as us. We're going to form a campaign that includes them, all of the unions, the churches, and every individual who is affected. We're going to organise a special train to take us down to London and march to Parliament. We're going to be peaceful, disciplined – and determined. Come and join us to London, bring your families, your kids. Because it's their future we're fighting for."

The meeting closed at 9.45 and we adjourned to Th' Kickin' Donkey just up the road. I sat down with Tommy over a pint and looked him in the eye. "So what's all this about a special train to London then, Tommy?"

"Well lad, I had to say summat didn't I? And what's the point o'traipsin' reaund Horwich or Bowton wi' banners and placards? We need to get deawn theer and mek some fuss."

The following day we had a special Works Committee. It was agreed that we organise a special train to take us all down to London - and that we invite the whole town to join us. Every member of The Works Committee was told to start raising money for the campaign. We had small fighting fund that amounted to about £400. To run the train alone we'd need double that.

The first fundraiser of our action committee - 'Save Horwich Loco' - was a folk night in the RMI Club, right opposite the Works gate. This was the descendant of the 'Railway Mechanics Institute', long since demolished. Unlike its dry predecessor it had a bar and a huge concert room. It was packed. The local morris dancers had agreed to perform for free and lots of local musicians did the same. Jimmy Calderbank, from the Paint Shop, was a local dialect poet when he wasn't painting wagons and carriages. He recited a poem he'd written specially.

"Ah'm not used to recitin' i'front o'sich a big crowd," he announced, apologetically. "Ah wrote this t'other neet when we heard as some of the other workshops weren't for backin' us. It's cawd 'Tommy Platt's Prophecy' an ah hope as it doesn't come true."

The concert room went quiet apart from the clinking of a couple of glasses, Tommy cleared his voice.

"Reet -

Tommy Platt were a fitter on t'railway
At Horwich were apprentic'd to th'trade
Til one day he geet a short letter:
"Thanks for your forty year's service" –

An' next month redundant were made.
He remembered when Horwich were famous
All o'er the owd LMS
For buildin' fine locos an' wagons
But neaw it's an 'ell of a mess.

Union said they'd feyt th'closure to th'finish
Mek a stond for th'whole of the teawn
'Cause if th'Loco Works goos there'll be nothin'
Sin th'mills an' the pits had shut deawn.

So they set up an action committee,
Wrote letters to every MP
Appealed to their own fellow workers
At Derby, Crewe an' Eastleigh

But t'other shops just wouldn't listen
Thowt their jobs 'ud be more secure
Took Horwich's workload – an' Shildon's
So closure for them became sure.

Tommy clocked eawt the last Friday
Wi th'mates he'd bin with forty year
Some daft bugger suggested a party
There wouldn't be much party fun theer.

As he walked throo th'gates for th'last time
Television cameras were theer
They axed Tommy fert comment on th'closure
An' a prophecy came through a tear.

"They shut deawn Ashford and Gorton
Neaw Horwich an' Shildon 've gone too.
We wain't be the last, that's for certain.
Watch eawt Swindon an' Crewe."

After two years on th'dole queue at Horwich
A teawn that were neaw good as dead
They anneaunced a new set o'closures
Seven theausand to goo, th'news said.

So them chaps as thowt they had jobs for life
At Doncaster, Derby an' Crewe
Were under the hammer theirsels neaw.
Tommy's prophecy had come true".

"Well done Jimmy," Tommy Hindley in his role as MC said. "But we're
not beat yet. And tha's reet owd lad, if they do shut us deawn, we won't
be th'last. Reet, let's have a break. Th'bars oppen and all tonight's proceeds
go to th'campaign. So gerremin."

We raised about £1500 that night. We were getting there.

Midge had volunteered to organise the special train from BR. She knew
a couple of blokes from her union in the offices in Manchester who made
sure we got a cheap rate. She reported to the next meeting of the
campaign committee.

"It's all sorted out. Tuesday September 12th. Leaves Chorley at 06.30,
stops to pick up at Adlington, Blackrod and Bolton. We arrive at Euston
at 10.30. It's a 12 coach train and we've room for 700. We'll have a lobby
of Parliament at 12.00. Bring your own food. And I've done a good deal
with the special trains unit, we've got it for £300."

"Well done Midge," Tommy said. "But how are we going to get down to
Parliament from Euston? It'll be a nightmare getting on th' Tube?"

"Tube? We're going to march! We'll bring our union banners, church
banners, we'll make placards. Horwich Band has already said they'll come
and lead us off from Euston Station. We'll mek a gradely show, believe
me!"

14

Parliament lobbied

Tickets for the train sold out within a couple of weeks. The local schools agreed to close down for the day and encouraged the children to go down with their mums, dads, aunties and uncles. They even set to making their own banners.

"My dad wants his job – Save Horwich Works' one said. "Don't put my mum on the dole" shouted another, from Esther, the 7-year old daughter of Vanessa from typing.

The Works Committee told management what was happening. The boss, Mr Barlow, wasn't too pleased about a day of lost production but he and his management team could see the sense of it – like everyone else, they'd be affected the same as everyone else if the Works closed down, so one day wouldn't make much difference.

Most of the marchers joined the train at their nearest station, Blackrod. "We'll assemble at 06.00 at the Works gate," Tommy announced, "and march behind Horwich Band down to the station. Bring your banners and placards. And just one thing. No drinkin' on th'way deawn. We're going to go into Parliament sober, that understood, reet?"

There were a few moans and groans from the shop stewards but they could see his point. "We'll mek up for it on th'road back," Jack Halliwell said to his mate and fellow boozer Joe Cornthwaite, with a wink.

Les Highson and mate

The 12th September dawned without a cloud in the sky, unusual for Horwich. About 400 of us assembled by the Works gate, with the band tuning up and the banner of the Joint Shop Stewards Committee unfurled. There were other banners too, from the NUR, AEU, electricians, Boilermakers' Society, TSSA and Transport and General. Midge and her mate Sandra Walker were holding up the TSSA banner, amidst all the blokes. But there were church banners too, and lots of makeshift designs saying 'Save Our Works' and the like. We set off in good spirits, assisted by our local bobby Joe Jolly and marched down Crown Lane to the station. The band started off with 'Hail Smiling Morn' and progressed to 'Colonel Bogey', 'When the Saints Go Marching In' and 'Men of Harlech'. We felt proud – of our work, and of our community. Of our class. My mum always used to say that hearing a brass band made her cry – and I could understand why as we walked down Crown Lane to get our train.

It took us longer than we'd thought and the train was just coming into view as the first of us arrived on the platform. Midge had brought some of her fellow councillors, including Councillor 'Chip Butty' Greenhalgh.

"Are you not opening the shop tonight then Jimmy?" I enquired.

"What's the point lad, everyone'll be in London! But I wanted to show my support anyroad."

Our train was hauled by a big class 47 diesel loco complete with a specially made headboard – "SAVE HORWICH LOCO WORKS". As the train approached, the driver gave a special rendition of 'Ilkley Moor Baht' 'At' on his horn. Leaning out of the cab was former Bolton driver Bert Westby who'd transferred to Preston when the shed closed a few years back. He was in his element. The secondman was another ex-Bolton lad, Jim Whitehead.

"Are you comin' all th' way wi' us Bert?" Tommy shouted up.

"Wish we were owd lad but they'll put a leccy on at Stockport. A bit faster than us. And I've only got me road signed as far as Crewe."

Everyone slowly piled on and the guard blew his whistle, getting a bit impatient and worrying about losing time. Twice as many people waved us off as got on the train, some with makeshift signs and banners saying "Good Luck Horwich!" Bert gave another noisy display as we set off; some of the apprentices had put down a few detonators on the track to give an added bit of fireworks. They'd told the driver what to expect so he ignored the succession of explosions as the wheels of the loco passed over them.

The only other stop was Bolton. We pulled in to see a big crowd waiting with the Trades Council banner prominently displayed - and many more, including the textile workers, printers, bleachers and dyers and engineers.

We had a compartment with Terry Dukinfield from the Paint Shop and his wife Marjorie who ran a fancy goods place on Lee Lane, old Ezra Liptrot, long since retired from the Erecting Shop and bent double with arthritis. There was another woman, in her late 50s I'd say but quite smart looking, despite wearing jeans and jacket complete with a 'Save Horwich Works' badge. Midge was the first to recognise her.

"Isn't it Mrs Barlow?" Midge enquired. She was the husband of George Barlow, the Works Manager, George had served his time at Horwich after the war and moved around to various railway Workshops, first as a fitter and then going into management – at Derby, Crewe and Darlington. When Darlington was down to close he applied, and got, the top job at Horwich and had run the place since 1971.

"Yes that's right – I think I've seen you in the office when I've been in to see George. How do you do? My name's Enid by the way."

"And I'm Midge, and this is David who Works in the Smithy, Terry and Marjorie, and Ezra. "Oh yes I know Mr Liptrot, I was with my husband George when we presented you with a 40 year medal, do you remember?"

"Ah do that, and th' clock he gan me still keeps perfect time!"

Mrs Barlow, or for that matter her husband, didn't have a high profile in the town, though she was a member of the Methodist church choral society. Their performances of 'Messiah' each Christmas packed the church hall. Her husband played violin in the Horwich Orchestral Society.

"So you're on your own then today?" Midge asked slightly coyly.

"Oh yes, George has to stay in the office, it wouldn't do for him to be seen on a demonstration, it's not really him anyway. But I wanted to come and show my support, so I'm really here on behalf of us both."

"Well, if the Works closes it'll affect you as much as it does us," Midge suggested.

"Well not really. George is coming up for retirement and he'll get a good railway pension. No, it's not about us, it's about this community. That's why I'm here, not out of self-interest. But – oh, I'm sorry I'm not suggesting you're here just for yourselves."

"Well, we don't want to lose our jobs, but it's about more than that, like you say."

We wound our way through the Manchester suburbs and reached Stockport, where our diesel was uncoupled and ran back past the train with Bert and Dave hanging out of the cab waving their caps and sounding their horn as they went.

"Daft buggers," said Midge, trying not to laugh.

The electric loco dropped down from the sidings and coupled on to our train and we were away, next stop London.

Terry and Marjorie were good company, Ezra didn't say much but Mrs Barlow – who insisted on being called Enid – slowly came out of her reserve.

"I've brought some sandwiches and a few little cakes that I baked last night," she smiled. "Would anyone care to try one?"

Ezra greedily leapt forward and grabbed a big slice of Victoria Sponge. "Ah forgeet to'get mi breakfast this morn....this'll do t'job." We dipped into the dainty display of sandwiches, me opting for the cheese and chutney whilst Midge tried one with ham and mustard.

Midge and Enid got on well with each other, chatting about their choral singing, how they'd manage without the Works, and also about their shared love of rambling.

"We've always been keen walkers," said Enid. "I was brought up in Derby, where I met George. My playground was the Peak District and we used to go out on the train most Sundays. Happy days. But I love the hills around Horwich – Rivington, Anglezarke, Great Hill. They aren't as dramatic as the Peak District but they have a peacefulness and solitude to them."

"Yes, I used to go out with my late husband most weekends up those hills, when we weren't off out on the bikes."

"Ah, Mr Wrightson. That was a terrible tragedy, you must have been heartbroken," Enid said. "George was deeply upset. He has a tendency to blame himself for everything and he has never forgiven himself for not having that crane checked."

"It wasn't anyone's fault," said Midge. "He mustn't feel like that. And it was years ago. But you never quite get over it, even if he was a bit hard at times."

Erecting Shop with Overhead Crane

We passed Stoke-on-Trent, Lichfield, Rugby, Bletchley. The landscape became richer, the houses bigger and more neatly laid-out. We passed the London suburbs: Watford, Bushey, Harrow and Wealdstone flashed past. We'd be in London in 10 minutes.

We arrived at Euston a couple of minutes early. In good traditional style we'd had a whip-round for the driver, secondman and guard – Manchester men, from Longsight and Piccadilly – who gave us all a friendly wave and blast on the horn as we trooped up the ramp with our banners and placards.

Tommy Hindley was in charge of the arrangements and had planned the route with the police well before. Some of the coppers were a different kettle of fish from our local bobbies like Jimmy, whose wife was on the march with us. They looked miserable bastards, spoiling for a fight. They weren't going to get one though, not today.

We were joined at Euston by some of the more militant NUR members from London District Council. There was a token presence from the national executive, led by the deputy general secretary Derek Shaw, a former signalman from Tyneside. Pete Jagger, one of my party friends and a member of the district council, had just come off his early shift – he was a guard at Euston depot – and was going to join us. He was still in uniform, complete with his guard's leather bag.

We set off across Euston Road to toots from the taxi drivers and angry glares from the some of the car drivers forced to wait a few minutes while we got across.

"You bastards are ruining this country!" one of them yelled out of the safety of his car window.

Some of the women blew him a kiss. "Remember now, don't respond to any provocation," Tommy reminded us from his megaphone.

Most of the people who watched as we marched down Tottenham Court Road were either nonplussed or supportive. Some of the shopworkers came out and applauded. Office workers, even a few city gents who still sported bowler hats, gave us friendly waves.

When the coppers realised we weren't intent on violent revolution, for the time being, they relaxed a bit and some shared fags with the stewards. Enid had got into her stride by now and was leading the chanting.

"What do we want?

"Keep Our Jobs!"

"When do we want 'em?"

"Now!!"

Yeah. Lacking in originality I know but it sent out the message to anyone who cared to listen. I tried to make up a good chant that rhymed with 'Horwich' but the best I could do was something about porridge.

A few hangers-on from the SWP were selling their papers and shouting 'General Strike – Now!' but they didn't raise much of a noise, or support. It took us nearly an hour to get near to Parliament; we could see 'Big Ben' peeping out beyond the government buildings on Whitehall. Time to strike up the band again. The lads – and a few lasses – were in good form playing 'Rimington' as we passed the gates to Downing Street. "Come on, play 'The Red Flag'" we all implored. They obliged - it's not a brilliant anthem but does go well played by a brass band. My mum would have been in tears by now.

We stopped in Parliament Square and our local MPs were there to meet us – Albert Smith, ageing Labour member for Horwich and his younger pal Gary Stewart, for Bolton North. They were joined by Tom Simmons, the Tory for the newly-created seat of Westhoughton Central, which we all thought sounded like a railway station. About 50 of us had got clearance to go into the House of Commons itself, though most were happy enough to sit on the grass, eat our sandwiches and get slowly pissed.

Albert Smith was introduced by Tommy Hindley. There was no love lost between either of them but the day demanded unity and toleration.

"Brothers and sisters, I'm delighted that our local MP Albert Smith has put aside vital parliamentary business and come to address us. Mr Smith..."

"Well thank you Tom, thank you. Yes, well I've been your member of parliament for Horwich over 40 years now and we've seen a few changes. As you know, I started my working life in the Loco Works and served my time in the Machine Shop before going to fight for King and Country. When I was elected in 1945 we had high hopes for our railways as part of the new Britain, and one of the first things the new Labour Government did was to nationalise them. We had ten years of growth and modernisation, but the tide was turning against the railways as people bought their cars. You can't halt progress. But we need to carry on building trains and for me, they should be built at Horwich. Let 'em close down Doncaster if they want, there are jobs in the coal mines..."

At this point some of the crowd was starting to get restless. Johnny Gregson, one of the more volatile shop stewards, shouted out "No workshops should close! We're not here to put other people out o'work!" A lot of voices piped up in support of Johnny.

"Come on lads, let Mr Smith finish," pleaded Tommy.

"Well yes, as I was saying. Let's face facts. We can't halt progress. I'm with you in your campaign but you know what the best way of succeeding is? I'll tell you. Elect a Labour Government. Thank you chairman."

Next to speak was Gary Stewart. He'd been MP for a few years and was parachuted in by Labour's Executive as a rising star. He'd been a lawyer in Birmingham before then and spoke with a mild Brummy accent. He hadn't shown much interest in the campaign so far but he knew his seat was marginal and didn't want to lose his job in a year or two.

"I'm delighted to welcome this amazing crowd to Parliament. I was moved to tears as I saw your banners coming down Whitehall...."

"Spare me, for Christ's sake", whispered Midge, who'd never liked him. "Only time he'd be moved to tears is if he lost his seat, or got de-selected."

"The fight to save Horwich Works has got to be won," he continued. "Like my colleague Albert says, the surest way to succeed is to elect a Labour Government and give Thatcher her marching orders.."

"It were Labour that finished off Beeching's dirty work!" shouted Ernie Eccleston from the middle of the crowd. Tha meyt be too young to remember it, but ah con!"

Stewart mumbled a few more platitudes about taking the case up with the Prime Minister and stood down. Applause was polite, but muted.

"Thank you Gary, we appreciate your support. Our final speaker is Tom Simmons, the Conservative MP for Westhoughton Central. Please give Mr Simmons a respectful hearing."

Simmons was greeted by a few groans and hisses from some of the young lads but people nudged them to be quiet and "give the lad a hearing" as Tommy urged.

And he was a lad really, probably in his late 20s. He came from one of the old Lancashire families and owned half of Pendle Forest. He looked nervous and you could hardly blame him.

"Thank you very much Mr Chairman, and thank you for coming down to London to make your voices heard. I suppose most of you didn't vote for me (cries of "Too bloody right!") and that's your privilege. But I was elected to serve all the people of my constituency, which almost touches on the Works site. Many of you live in Westhoughton and I understand how serious this threat is, to both Horwich and its neighbouring town. My only connection with the railways was my father, who was a director of the LMS. Yes, I'm from a privileged background but that doesn't mean to say I'm not going to stand up for what I believe is right. And you are right to fight this closure and I'll do everything in my power to help you win. I've an appointment tomorrow morning with the Transport Minister and I'm going to urge he changes his mind and instructs – and I mean 'instructs' – the British Railways Board to halt this closure. I don't believe in keeping factories going that have no future, but I'm convinced there is a future for Horwich Loco Works, doing what it does well – building trains. And if there is anything more I can do to help you, please just ask."

He got a round of respectful applause. Of all three he sounded the most sincere. And he was right, there were no votes for him in this.

Midge had got a pass to go into Parliament to see her MP, the less than charismatic Mr Smith. I'd been delegated to stay outside and steward the crowd. Which meant no drink, at least for the first half hour, or so. Pete had managed to get a pass so he could lobby his own MP, from one of the inner London suburbs, on the need for rail investment. I watched him trotting off by the St Stephen's entrance, looking forward to a cheap pint in the Stranger's Bar.

About 10 minutes later I heard a siren going off and lots of police suddenly appeared, with very real-looking machine guns.

"What the fuck's goin' on?" one of my mates asked.

"Don't know but it sounds like some sort of security alert. Hope it's nowt to do with us."

About half an hour later Pete emerged from the gates, assisted by two very heavy and serious-looking coppers. He looked unusually sheepish.

"What's happened?" I asked him.

"Well comrade it's all a bit embarrassing. I'd forgotten I had the can of dets in my guard's bag and it triggered off an alarm. When the cops opened the bag they found what to them looked like dangerous explosives. It took me a lot of effort to persuade them that they were railway detonators that you put on the track if your train had broken down to warn other trains of the obstruction. Fortunately one of the coppers was ex-railway and he recognised them. He said I was a stupid cunt and was bloody lucky not to be arrested and sent down for carrying dangerous weapons into Parliament. Said the last bloke to do that was Guy Fawkes and you know what happened to him."

"Well for once I agree with the coppers," I told him. "Putting the uncalled-for sexist language aside, you are a fucking stupid bastard aren't you? And I suppose you'll be asking me for one of these bottles of ale now?"

About an hour and three more bottles of Newcastle Brown later, Midge re-appeared.

"How did it go love?" I asked, nonchalantly, with Pete sat next to me all smiles.

"Oh it was alright. The interview was cut short because of some sort of security alert. Did you hear anything about it? There were armed police running round all over the place."

"No love, not a thing. Did you hear anything Pete?"

"No, nothing."

"What makes me think you're a couple of lying little buggers? But anyway, it felt like we were going through the motions. He said he'd come along to the next Action Committee meeting and ask questions in The House."

Our train was booked off Euston at 18.45, after the rush-hour had finished and giving us time to see some of the sights. A few of the lads said they were off to a strip club in Soho. Midge was caustic.

"About time you lot grew up, ogling some naked young woman. You should be ashamed of yourselves."

"It's only a bit o' fun," said Jack Milligan, from the Foundry.

"Oh, right Jack, I'm sure your missus will agree when I mention it to her at the club on Saturday?"

"You wouldn't, would you?"

"You just wait and see. Anyroad, they cost an arm and leg to get in those places, you couldn't afford it."

The group of intending revellers slunk off, ending up in one of the pubs near Euston where they made a nuisance of themselves singing 'She's a Lassie from Lancashire' and 'Daisy' in an exuberant display of local pride. Funny how the really corny old songs suddenly spring up when you're pissed, and you can remember every line.

It was a warm September day so we wandered down to the Thames Embankment with Enid and a few of the girls from the Typing Pool, including Vanessa.

"You know what we should do next time?" Vanessa asked of no-one in particular. "We should circle the House of Commons, with everyone holding hands saying 'Ommmmm.' And we should then get the place to levitate. It'd show them the spiritual power of the people."

"There's a few flaws in your strategy," I suggested. "For one thing the Houses of Parliament face on to the River Thames on one side, so we'd get a bit wet trying to encircle the place. And what would you do after the place had been raised up a few feet? Let it fall down again?"

"Well OK, I know the idea seems slightly wacky and needs a bit more thought, but we do need to be more imaginative than just asking boring MPs for a few favours."

"Well that's for sure," said Midge. "I'm not sure what we've achieved from this junket but at least we've tried."

It was coming up to 6.00 so we headed for the Tube and squeezed onto a train heading for Euston. We needed to be in good time to marshal the crowd and look out for any strags. The train would leave on the dot at 6.45, whether everyone was on or not.

The gate opened to let us onto the platform at 6.30 and Midge and her mate Erica from accounts ticked everyone off as they went on. By 6.40 we were missing just three.

"It's those stupid buggers who were after going to that strip club!" Midge groaned. "Just wait til I get my hands on them."

At 6.43 there was a commotion on the concourse and the three lads – Jack Milligan, Joey Sumner and Graham Thwaite – ran down the ramp to the platform - pissed out of their heads - singing 'Show me the way to go home...'

"Oh Midge, Mrs Wrightson, don't be cross with us, we got on the wrong train and ended up in bloody Walthamstow or somewhere....And I'm dying for a piss..."

"Well you're not pissing here, get on this bloody train, it's about to set off."

We dragged them onto the train and the guard raised his green flag, whistled, and we felt the tug of the loco as we set off for home.

We were all knackered, apart from Enid who seemed to have boundless energy. "Well what are we going to do next?" she asked. "We've got to plan a campaign that'll make them sit up! Remember the Suffragettes!"

"Yes Enid," Midge replied. "But we don't want to be chaining ourselves to railings or throwing ourselves under horses. But I'm buggered if I do know what we should do."

"I know what!" said Enid. "Remember a few years ago the workers up in Glasgow who faced the same issue with the closure of their shipyard? They took over the yard and started a work-in. Why don't we do that at Horwich?"

"You mean Upper Clyde Shipbuilders – UCS - ?" I asked.

"Yes, that's it. Wasn't one of the leaders a communist, like you?"

"Er yes, Jimmy Reid. A great guy. And a few more beside. So you're saying we should take over the Works and run it ourselves?"

"Yes, that's exactly what I'm saying!"

"Wow, that's really far out," said Vanessa, who'd joined us in our compartment.

"Well I think it's a good idea," said Midge. "It needs a lot of thought and careful planning. And they haven't actually said the Works is going to close on any particular date. It's out for 'consultation', which we know is just part of the game that we can't win."

"Right then Midge," I said as we whizzed through Wolverton, whose railway works was a shadow of its former self, employing a few hundred where thousands once worked. "Are you going to raise this as a firm proposal at tomorrow's meeting of the Action Committee?"

"Too right I am!"

"That's just so...far out," sighed Vanessa as she fell asleep across Midge's lap. She didn't wake up until we got to Stockport.

15

The decision to occupy

"You want us to do what?" Tommy Hindley said to Midge. They were in the Labour Club bar on Wednesday evening, before the meeting of the Action Committee. "Take over the factory? Have you joined the SWP or summat? Or just gone mad?"

"What other chance have we got?" Midge asked him. "The Works will close unless we do something drastic. We can have as many marches to Parliament as we like but it isn't going to change their minds is it? Striking would be futile, just hastening the inevitable. But if we take the place over we might just be able to shame them into keeping us going. Who knows?"

"So you're saying we do a sort of UCS work-in then? Which might have some merit but there's a few differences. The Upper Clyde Shipbuilders work-in was back in the 70s. We didn't have a viciously right-wing government like we have now. And the UCS workers were a million times more militant than our people at Horwich. It's a totally different situation."

"Yes, I know it's different," Midge answered, "but what have we got to lose? Not everyone will be up for it I know and we can make sure that anyone who wants it can take their redundancy. But those that want to hang on to their jobs should have the chance." Midge replied.

"Well look. You raise it at the meeting this evening an' let's see what sort o' response you get. If there's a majority in support, ah'll back it."

"But will you speak in favour?" Midge pressed him.

"My job is to chair the meeting, not decide policy. I'll make sure everyone gets a fair hearing and go with the majority."

"Tommy Hindley, I don't know what your mother would think of you. She was a fighter – she set up the Independent Labour Party in Horwich and fought for women's suffrage. Your job is to lead, not go along with whoever shouts loudest."

"Aye, I know what tha's sayin' Midge. Let's see how the meeting goes. Ah'll say nowt more."

Erecting Shop, working on carriage frame

The members of the Action Committee drifted in to the meeting room just before 7.30, most with pints in their hands. The majority were members of the Works Committee – shop stewards and union reps – but there were people from the community as well. Father Martin O'Shaughnessy, the Catholic priest from St. Mary's, holding a pint of Guinness. Rupert Singleton, vicar of All Saints, the Anglican vicar, clutching a half of shandy and looking all too self-conscious. Eric Braithwaite, owner of the local pet shop, was there with his pint, together with Marjorie Brierley from the knitting shop on Lee Lane sipping a glass of orange and lemonade. More wandered in, with the room almost full to capacity by 7.35. Tommy stood up.

"Good evening ladies and gentlemen. Thank you for coming along to this meeting of the Save Horwich Loco Works Action Committee. We had a highly successful demonstration and lobby of Parliament yesterday. We got excellent headline publicity in *The Bolton Evening News* and we featured in some of the national papers too. We got firm assurances from all three of our local MPs that they'd do all they can to help our campaign. Negotiations between the unions and the management are now at a delicate stage and we are pressing hard for a settlement that safeguards train building in Horwich. But we need to keep the pressure on. So can I have views from the floor please?"

Harry Alker, one of the stewards from the Paint Shop, rose to speak. He was one of the older union activists with nearly 40 years service and a good pension to look forward to.

"Well Mr Chairman I have to say it was an excellent day and we have put Horwich on the map. But I remain of the view that the only way forward is to get the best possible redundancy deal for the Works' employees. We can't save train building at Horwich. Places like Darlington and Gorton have closed, despite all the hoo-ha. We can't win. So I say we admit we've fought the good fight and go for the best possible severance terms."

Johnny was quickly on his feet to argue for more militant action. "That's all very well for Brother Alker to say we should go for a redundancy settlement. He's got his time in. Many of us have less than five years' service and we'll get next to nowt. I say we lobby our union leaderships for an all-out rail strike to save all the threatened railway workshops."

Midge had her hand up and Tommy called her to speak.

"Brothers and sisters, and friends from our local community. We need to think this through carefully. On one hand we should recognise that some of the workforce just want to get their redundancy and call it a day. Fair do's. But there are lots more who want to keep their jobs. We can't all transfer to Derby, Glasgow or Crewe. But how do we do stop the Works closing? I can't see a cat in hell's chance of the unions calling an all-out rail strike to save Horwich. We'd be lucky even to get them to support a one-day strike and what use would that be? Management would shrug it off and save money from not paying people to work. There is another option that we should think about. Back in 1971 workers at Upper Clyde Shipbuilders were faced with the same situation and they said they weren't willing to see their jobs go. They occupied the shipyard and carried on working. Eventually management and the unions, backed by the Government, did a deal and the yards are still going today. I know, there are far fewer workers employed. But there is still shipbuilding on the Clyde and that was down to the workers doing what they did. It can work here, in Horwich."

The response to Midge's intervention was silence, initially.

Then Father O'Shaughnessy stood up.

"I think this is a marvellous suggestion. The railway workers of Horwich want to work. They want to safeguard their jobs, for their children's future. They don't want to consign their children to a life on the dole or stacking supermarket shelves. I think Mrs Wrightson's suggestion is inspired by the Holy Spirit. It must be tried."

"Well I think she's inspired by a different sort of spirit, father, with all due respect," said Harold Aspinall, one of the Machine Shop stewards. "We would be breaking the law and we'd risk our redundancy payments. I can't see our union leadership supporting this for one minute. And the people who led the UCS work-in were all communists I'd have you know, father."

At that point a voice from the back of the room piped up. "Mr Chairman, could I say a few words please?" It was Tom Simmons, the Conservative MP for Westhoughton Central. "Nobody could accuse me of being a communist. I've been a Conservative all my life and my parents, grand-parents and previous generations were all True Blue. But I have to say that Mrs Wrightson's suggestion is worthy of consideration. I have raised the Horwich Loco Works issue with Government ministers and they say it is for British Rail to agree a solution, and they don't wish to interfere. As a member of this Government I have to respect that position. But the very strong risk is that the Works will close and hundreds – thousands – will be out of work. The effect on local businesses will be catastrophic. The town will die. So I hesitate to say this, but a peaceful, orderly work-in might be the way to secure future employment."

Several people around the room applauded. Tommy Hindley rose up from his chair, as several hands shot up to speak. "We have a very serious proposal here and it isn't something we should adopt – or reject – without detailed consideration. My suggestion is that we agree to look at the proposition in more detail and report back to a meeting of this committee in two weeks' time. Is that acceptable to the meeting?"

The general view was that Tommy's suggestion made sense. A small sub-committee was formed from the Action Committee including Tommy as chair, Midge, the Tory MP and his Labour counterpart Albert Smith, Father O'Shaughnessy, and four of the shop stewards, including myself and Harold Aspinall.

The Lounge, Horwich RMI Club

We were to meet in the back room of the RMI Club a few days later. We had a few days to work with the idea up into some semblance of viability, but keeping it as much to ourselves as we could. Midge had got the bit between her teeth by now and we'd talked the idea through at home, and with some of my party comrades. The view from our own party was cautious support. The district secretary, Peter Lennon, was encouraging. I met him, with Midge, in a pub near Victoria station in Manchester the following night.

"It's a great idea, but what are you trying to achieve? Is it a tactic to get BR to agree better terms, or maybe keep some operations going at Horwich? Or is it more ambitious? Are you trying to run your own factory? You need to decide these things and then go for it. We control many of the works committees across the Manchester engineering industry – at GEC, Gardners, Crossleys – they would support you. The Manchester District Committee of the engineering union is party-dominated. And the NUR's Manchester District Council is on the left. They'll back you as well. But you've got to be clear on your aims."

I could see Midge's brain cells working overtime in response to Lennon's questions.

"You're right, we need to be clear. For my money we should try and run the place ourselves. We have the expertise to do it, as far as building trains goes. We'd need help on the business side. It'd be good to find out how the UCS fellas went on and what help they got. But why shouldn't we run our own factory. Wouldn't that be socialism in practice?"

We spent a couple of hours kicking the idea round and nearly ended up missing our last train back to Bolton. We jumped on the train as it was about to leave.

"We're taking on a bloody big proposition Midge, you know that?" I said as we snuggled up in the rattling diesel train as it left Victoria's platform 12.

"Well, are you up for it, or not?" she asked.

"Course I bloody well am," grabbing a kiss as we passed Moses Gate. "Viva the revolution!"

As it was Enid's idea in the first place, Midge decided to give her a ring to see if she'd like to talk about the plan, and maybe get her husband's view. She found the phone number from directory enquiries, recognising it as one of the bigger houses on Victoria Road, built in the 1890s for Works' managers.

"Oh hello Enid...Mrs Barlow...it's Midge Wrightson here. We've been thinking about the idea of a work-in and I wonder if you'd like to meet up for a cup of tea to discuss it?"

Enid suggested meeting at the Cottage Tea Rooms in Horwich the following day, being a Saturday. "Lovely, see you there at 11.00."

Enid arrived on the dot, looking a bit like an East German spy – dark glasses, short hair, trouser suit and briefcase. "Oh hello Mrs Wrightson, it's very nice to see you again. Excuse the glasses but I'd rather not have too many people seeing me. This is all a bit sensitive."

"Oh that's understood. So shall we get back to first name terms? What would you like to drink Enid? Earl Grey Tea? And a nice scone?"

Enid had been doing a lot of thinking about her idea and she'd obviously talked it through with her husband, who had overall responsibility for any orders placed with the Works. "The trouble is Midge, all the orders currently come from within British Rail – wagons, carriages and sundries. So we'd be very dependent on the good will of BR. That isn't to say we couldn't broaden out and go into new markets, in the UK and abroad for that matter. But it takes time. It wouldn't be easy. But George says he will do all he can to help. And he's coming up for retirement soon and will have more time on his hands."

"Right, so does he think we could persuade BR to keep giving Horwich some work if we were an independent concern?"

"Well, at this stage he doesn't know. It's possible, but they'll be after sending most of the work to their own remaining workshops at Crewe, Derby and Glasgow. Unless Horwich could offer a good deal."

The next three days we spent in Bolton Library going through everything we could find about worker co-operatives and the international market for railway rolling stock. The Co-operative Union had its own research facilities in Manchester so we spent Saturday afternoon there. As well as the UCS example, we found other cases of workers taking over their own factories and – in some cases – making a go of them. But most of them were small concerns of less than 100 workers. Horwich still had a payroll of nearly 2,000.

The meeting of the full Action Committee heard a detailed report from Midge on the options for a work-in leading to an employee buy-out.

"It won't be easy but we could make it work. First of all we need to capture the headlines by taking direct action and occupying the factory, like they did at UCS. It's a bit risky and we could end up having the police on our backs. But going to BR and asking them to hand over the place to us is cloud-cuckoo-land. They wouldn't do it and the union leaderships wouldn't be any help. We're on our own. But we need to get BR into a position where they give us the factory as a going concern and we run it as a workers' co-operative. Sounds straightforward but it won't be, I can tell you that."

"Thank you Midge, that's a very clear exposition of the possibilities. Can I have questions and comments?"

There was no shortage of questions and opinion. Some of the older end just wanted to take the money. Some of the younger shop stewards thought it was worth a go – what had they to lose? They weren't going to up sticks and move to Crewe or Derby. The community folk, including the clerics and shopkeepers, wanted the Works to stay open at all cost.

"If we're running the place as a workers' co-operative we can give priority wherever possible to local suppliers," argued Midge. Whether it's catering, stationery or bigger stuff like components let's buy local wherever we possibly can."

The one dissenting voice came from the Labour MP Albert Smith, despite being sponsored by the Co-operative Party. "What Mrs Wrightson is suggesting is backdoor privatisation. We're being asked to take the Works out of British Rail ownership as a separate entity and that means workers would lose standard terms and conditions."

"What we stand to lose, with all respect Mr Smith, is our jobs. So standard terms and conditions would be irrelevant if we had no jobs to apply them to."

"Mr Chairman, this is a very big step for us to take," said Jim Lee, our local party secretary. Can I suggest we take the idea back to the shopfloor and offices and see what the feeling of the workforce is? After a week we can have a further meeting to review the feeling in the Works and agree on action then."

"That sounds a very good suggestion Jim. So, is that agreed that the shop stewards and union reps have shop meetings to put the idea of a work-in, leading to a workers' buyout, be taken forward by the Action Committee, and that community representatives ask their own people if they would support us?"

The meeting agreed, unanimously, to accept the proposal and meet again in a weeks' time.

"And can I ask everyone, as far as you possibly can, don't make a big song and dance of this, it mustn't get into the press, if we can avoid it."

Wheel Shop

After the meeting had closed, Simmons, the Tory MP, came up to Tommy Hindley with a suggestion.

"Mr Hindley, would you mind if I approached some of my friends in the business community and see if you can get some help on the commercial and legal side of doing this? You have the technical skills but you don't have the business expertise, if you don't mind me saying."

"Well thanks, that's appreciated, and I don't mind you being up front with us. Why not make some informal soundings and see if there's people out there who can help us? But we don't have any money to pay consultants' fees."

"No don't worry about that, it'll be pro bono."

"Pro what?" Tommy asked, "sounds like some sort of dog food."

"For free!"

16

With Jimmy Reid and Airlie

The response from the shopfloor was mixed. The younger end were all for occupying. Most of the older blokes were scared shitless about jeopardising their pensions. If they could get a bit extra with a redundancy package, they'd be happy. There was a narrow majority for occupying the Works, if BR was determined to close the place down.

The Works Committee was to hold a special meeting of all the shop stewards in advance of the fortnightly Action Committee meeting on October 16th, a Wednesday. The decision to occupy - or not - would be taken by the Works Committee, acting on behalf of the membership.

Tommy, Midge, myself and some of the senior stewards took a day out to travel to Glasgow the previous week to meet some of the guys that had been involved in the UCS work-in. They had saved shipbuilding on the Clyde, but only a fraction of the workforce remained. I'd helped to fix up the meeting, through the Party. Most of the work-in leaders were Communist Party – Jimmy Reid, Jimmy Airlie and others. Our Manchester party office got in touch with Glasgow and it was all arranged.

Jimmy Reid, now retired from UCS, arranged to meet us off the train at Glasgow Central. To me he was a legendary figure.

There was a car waiting outside the station and we were soon on our way to the university. "Great to meet you boys – and – Midge isn't it? - Thanks for coming. I've fixed up a room at the university for us. One of the perks o'bein' Rector! We'll get ye something tae eat as well".

Reid was knowledgeable about Horwich. "I've heard about the Works and your campaign. The march on Parliament was brilliant. You've got the community on side, great. You're doing all the right things. But ye're no gonnae win, are ye, unless ye dae somethin' that'll really shake them? What we did at UCS isn't always the answer. We had our backs tae the wall, believe me. If we hadnae occupied that would've been it. We didnae get everythin' we wanted but we saved a lot of the jobs. An' they're still building ships on the Clyde."

We arrived at the university and our little group was escorted into the Rector's Office by Reid. We were met there by some of the senior stewards who had been involved in the work-in at UCS. A couple were in the same engineering union as Tommy and Joe Vince, one of our senior stewards.

Reid invited us to sit round the board room table. "It shows what progress we've made, hey? Trade unionists sitting down in a place like this. And who wants tea, coffee? We'll have ye fed in the university refectory, but let's get down to business. Once we've sorted the drinks."

Tommy was a bit over-awed by the place. He'd left school at 15 and was glad to see the back of his school in Westhoughton, just as the teachers were glad to see the back of Tommy. He had no qualifications but was one of those blokes who was a real craftsman. He felt very at home with his Glasgow engineering brothers.

"Well Jimmy, let me just say that we really appreciate your support and time for talking to us. We aren't sure what we're letting ourselves in for so any honest advice in advance of our meeting next week would be priceless."

"We'll give ye honest advice, dinnae ye worry about that. It might not be what ye want tae hear, but we'll tell ye straight. Jimmy..." Reid introduced his comrade and fellow work-in leader Jimmy Airlie. "Jimmy here was the organising genius behind it all. I was just the front man who could talk tae the press. Ye need both. Jimmy, what can ye tell these comrades?"

"Thanks Jimmy, and ye're right, let's be honest. Would we have done it again in the same circumstances? Aye, I think we would. But it's very, very hard work. Ye'll make a lot of enemies but ye'll find a lot of friends. We got support from all over the world. But during the occupation, some of our own people in Glasgow hated us. If I was on fire in the street some of them wouldn't cross the road tae piss on me. Sorry sister, hope ye don't mind me being frank."

Midge was more amused by the metaphor than some of the other guys. "Don't worry about me Mr Airlie, I'm not easily offended."

"Aye, well ye'll get worse than that, believe me. But let's learn the lessons of history. Our university wasnae this place. It was the shipyards and engineering works on the Clyde. We learned our Marxism at the factory bench, and in the Young Communist League and workers' clubs in Partick and Govan. We were taught some strong lessons, through theory – Marx, Lenin and oor ain John Mclean - and we were taught practical lessons, through struggle. Rule One: be united. If your members are split, ye'll lose. Rule Two: win hearts and minds in the community. At UCS we got Catholic and Protestant – Fenians and Orangemen – on the same side. We got the shopkeepers, we got the ice cream sellers, pub landlords, the lot – on our side. Rule 3 – the press. We won over the media, locally here in Glasgow and the London press, mostly. Even *The Scotsman*. And if ye're goin' tae take over the factory, you've got to be whiter than white. No bevvying, no gambling, no messin' wi' the lassies, just like a Sunday School picnic. But it's no picnic, we can tell ye all that. So remember - anything that the right wing press can pick on, they will."

The discussion went on for nearly two hours. How to win over the reluctant members, how to keep up morale, building links across the country – and the world. Having a well-managed fighting fund. Maintaining discipline. Political support was crucial.

"Ye have tae recognise hard reality," said Reid. "We've a Tory Government in power at Westminster. Ye cannae just rely on support from Labour. Up here we've a few SNP MPs. They're sound enough, mostly. And Liberals like David Steel. They'll back you. But ye have tae grit your teeth and talk tae the Tories as well. It's them that has the power, for now."

We had lunch in the university refectory. Reid was a popular choice for rector amongst the students and several came up to him to say a friendly hello. His speech when elected was one of the most powerful pieces of political oratory I'd ever heard. *"A rat race is for rats. We're not rats. We're human beings"*.

His speech could have been written for us at Horwich. *"To appreciate fully the inhumanity of this situation, you have to see the hurt and despair in the eyes of a man suddenly told he is redundant, without provision made for suitable alternative employment, with the prospect in the West of Scotland, if he is in his late forties or fifties, of spending the rest of his life in the Labour Exchange. Someone, somewhere has decided he is unwanted, unneeded, and is to be thrown on the industrial scrap heap. From the very depth of my being, I challenge the right of any man or any group of men, in business or in government, to tell a fellow human being that he or she is expendable."*

Our train to Bolton left at 3.30. Reid and Airlie took us back to the station and waved us off. "If ye boys – and lassies – go for it, let us know and we'll mebbe pop down and see yez!" said Airlie as the train slowly eased out of platform 1.

"We'll tek you up on that lad, don't worry!" said Tommy.

We sat back in our seats and felt a bit dazzled by it all. "Bloody 'ell, " Tommy broke the silence. "Those guys know their stuff don't they? Tough buggers too. Do you think we're up to it?"

Midge was sat by the window, admiring the Tinto Hills as we left the industrial central belt and the train gathered speed through the Clyde valley towards Beattock Summit.

"Yes, they're an impressive bunch but they're working class people like us. We can do it but it's not going to be easy. And they're right – we have to make sure we have that broad support, outside the Works".

The trolley came round and Tommy put his hand in his pockets for a few cans of beer. We were soon across the border and entering Carlisle. Penrith, Shap, Lancaster. We left Preston, with the next stop announced as Bolton. As we sped past Blackrod we could see the smoke from the Loco Works in the distance – that long expanse of industry under threat, with Horwich behind and Rivington Pike rising up in the distance.

It sounds corny saying this, but we looked out of the train and felt a sense of responsibility to the poor bastards working and living there. Were they going to be thrown on Reid's industrial scrap heap? Were we expendable?

"So are we going to recommend we occupy?" I asked, saying what was going through everyone's minds.

"Course we bloody are! We're not going to let the Jocks say we were Sassenach cowards, are we?" said Tommy, finishing the last can of beer as the train passed Bullfield Sidings and the Gasworks, before pulling to a stop in Bolton's platform 3.

Working on an electric class 313 train, Erecting Shop

The following Wednesday the Works Committee met, during company time, in the RMI club. Tommy insisted on the 'no drink' rule.

"Well brothers and sisters, thank you for your attendance. You've all done a grand job holding shop meetings and getting the view of the members about what action we take. We've been doing a lot of work behind the scenes, talking to experts, and meeting the leaders of the UCS work-in up in Glasgow. The recommendation of the senior stewards is very clear. We occupy the factory and do all we can to maintain production. We want to bring the company to the negotiating table and keep production going at Horwich. Those that want to take the money can do, without any shame. We'll do all we can to assist anyone who wants to leave. We want everyone who stays on to be 100% behind the action. We'll have to be in for a long struggle with no guarantee of winning. We will need to have a continuous presence in the Works, 24 hours a day, seven days a week. We don't want the company trying to sneak in and take out any equipment. We're going to need teams of our people travelling round the country to drum up support. Any questions?"

Midge stood up before any of the doubters could get a look in. "The girls – ladies – in typing are up for it. Even Mrs Watson said she'd help type up a campaign newsletter! One of the girls in the Drawing Office is a great cartoonist and she'll help design it. The girls in the Canteen are fully in support. The town is behind us, word has already got round. So I hope you lads will be – men – and stand up for our jobs and community!"

Terry Nuttall, one of the Joiners Shop stewards, stood up to speak. "I've got 40 years' service in at this place and I'm ready to retire and play golf. Most of the lads of my age are the same. But we've got responsibilities. My lad's a draughtsman and he'll be out of a job, and Janey is expecting her first. What sort of future are they going to have? I say we accept the recommendation, if we go down we'll go down feytin'."

The mood of the meeting was obvious. After a few more responses, mostly in support, Tommy moved to the vote.

"The motion is that we mount an indefinite occupation of the factory, with the aim of maintaining a long-term future for the Works. The action will take effect as soon as BR issues its first redundancy notice. All those in favour?"

Of the 36 stewards and union reps present, 28 hands went up in favour.

"All those against?" There was silence.

"Any abstentions?" Eight hands were raised, mostly from some of the old hand stewards whose members were worried about their pensions.

"Right then," announced Tommy. "We've work to do. We'll report this to the Action Committee tomorrow evening and we'll issue a press statement immediately after that. Thank you for your attendance."

17

'An orderly and peaceful occupation'

The Action Committee arranged to meet at 7.30 in the RMI Club the following evening. As well as the Works shop stewards, it was swelled by the local clerics, some of the local councillors, two MPs , Albert Smith and Tom Simmons, and business people. Tommy had had a chat with Midge in the bar and asked her to speak on behalf of the Works Committee.

"You speak better than me Midge, and they're more likely to listen to a woman. Wilta do it?"

"Aye, if you like Tommy. Thanks for asking."

We squeezed into the committee room – it was Bingo night so the big room was booked. Tommy brought the meeting to order.

"Thank you for attending, ladies and gentlemen. This is a special meeting of the Action Committee and we've got some important news to give you. This campaign has always been about more than just our own jobs, it's been about the future of Horwich. So we need your support for what we're proposing. Midge – Councillor – Wrightson will fill you in on the proposals. Midge, please..."

"Thank you Tommy. As many of you know we've been having discussions on the shopfloor and in the offices about the best way forward to save the Works. A few of us have had talks with other trades unionists facing similar issues. It's not been an easy choice but just lobbying our MPs – and thank you Albert and Tom for being with us today – isn't going to achieve what we want, which is to maintain as many jobs at Horwich as we possibly can. So our proposal is this....."

You could hear a pin drop as Midge looked up to address the meeting.

"As soon as BR issues its first redundancy notice, we take over the factory. It will be 100% peaceful and orderly. There will be no damage to any property or equipment. The aim is to keep production going and we will be talking to BR about continuing to supply us with wagons and coaches for repair. We want to make sure that everyone's pension entitlement is protected and those who want to leave will be able to do so. It's a high risk strategy but it seems to us the only way of saving the Works and saving our jobs. We ask you to back us."

At first there was silence. Some of the people from outside the Works had heard rumours that something big was being planned, but – taking over the factory? That was revolutionary!

Harry Openshaw from the pet shop on Lee Lane was first to speak.

"By the bloody hell tha's gam, that's all ah con say. If that's what the workers say they're up for, who are we not to support 'em? Aye, the tradespeople of Horwich will back you all to the hilt. I'm president o' th' chamber of commerce an' we'll support you."

Father O'Shaughnessy was next up. "Blessed are those that hunger and thirst after righteousness...what you are doing is divinely inspired. The congregation of St Mary's will help you with collections, fund-raising, whatever. I'll write to the Bishop and get his support. Our prayers will be with you, but it's action you'll be needing, not prayers."

"Could I say a few words, Mister Chairman?" Albert Smith, the local Labour MP rose to speak. Oh bloody hell, Midge thought, hoping he wasn't about to pour cold water on the plan.

"As you all know, I had some doubts about this idea when it was first raised. I still think it's risky. But when I were a lad fighting the Nazis in the Ardennes, that were risky too. If you want to win, you've got to take risks. We can't sit back and see these Works close. I've raised the issue with ministers – together with my parliamentary colleagues Mr Stewart and Mr Simmons - and all I've got back has been nice words, that it's up to BR to discuss the issue with the unions, that they can't intervene. Of course they could, if they wanted to. So, as your MP, you have my full support ladies and gentlemen. All I would say is keep it orderly and peaceful. Don't let any of those hotheads from the far left cause trouble. Stay united."

There was a ripple of applause through the room. His Conservative neighbour, Tom Simmons, was next to speak. "Can I echo what Albert has said? We've met the transport minister, the employment minister and tried to get a meeting with the PM. But without some local pressure they will be very reluctant to do anything. Governments don't like being seen to intervene in an industrial dispute, even when jobs are at stake. But

I've been reading up about the UCS work-in on the Clyde. The Government did intervene, eventually, after it became politically impossible not to. The UCS workers were on every TV screen across the country, arguing for their jobs and communities. It was peaceful, it was reasonable. The Government had to respond positively."

Tommy took some more contributions, all positive. "Ladies and gentlemen it's clear that there is strong support for our proposal. Can I take a show of hands please? All those in favour of the workers' occupation, or work-in, please show..."

Every hand in the room went up. "I'll take that as a yes then," smiled Tommy. "But don't rush off to the bar just yet. I want volunteers for some sub-committees. We want help wi' press and publicity, fund-raising, business liaison, and legal. Any volunteers please?"

Gail Bainbridge, staff reporter from *The Horwich Examiner*, volunteered to set up a press and publicity committee. Harry Openshaw, pet shop and chamber of commerce, agreed to do business liaison. Joyce Sanderson from the baker's said she'd look after fund-raising. Herbert Morgan, from Morgan and Riley Solicitors on Lee Lane, said he'd help with the legal side. "We don't get many workers' occupations to deal with at the firm so we'll have to do a bit of reading-up, but we're property and commercial lawyers and we'll be able to help, I'm sure."

"Well thank you very much, everyone. Gail, could you and your press and publicity team work up a press release to issue first thing tomorrow? But keep it vague, we don't want BR to pre-empt anything we might do, do we?"

18

Community support

"Workers Vow to Fight Closure." We made the headlines of *The Bolton Evening News* the next day, with Tommy and Midge, chair and vice-chair of the Action Committee, both extensively quoted. They avoided using the term 'occupation', preferring 'work-in', but made it clear that any compulsory redundancies would be resisted. "We're determined to save train building at Horwich," Midge was quoted as saying. "We are preparing for a long struggle, which will be peaceful and good humoured.

The community is fully behind us, local businesses are backing us. The workers at the Loco Works are united."

Regional TV got wind of the story and Granada Reports sent a film crew up to Horwich to cover the story. Tommy and Midge were filmed by the Works gates and several 'vox pop' pieces were done on the Lee Lane. Father O'Shaughnessy was filmed outside his church and Harry Openshaw was interviewed inside his shop, with a parrot on his shoulder. "Ah'm gooin' to train him to say 'Save Horwich Loco Works'," Harold informed the cameras.

Bolton Clarion Cycling Club – passing Horwich Loco Works on a club run; Spring Smithy in the distance

Within days every shop in Horwich was displaying posters saying the same thing. Churches organised jumble sales, the local folk club organised another benefit concert to raise funds. The local Clarion cyclists organised a sponsored bike ride which raised £230.

The Works Committee carried on as normal, taking up the usual problems over promotion, sick pay, health and safety and the day-to-day stuff that shop stewards did. Tommy and Midge, and Joe Francis from the NUR, were summoned to meet the union leaderships in London to discuss the campaign.

They were to attend a special meeting at Unity House, the NUR headquarters, to meet the leaders of the main unions involved at the Works. Derek Shaw, the deputy leader of the NUR who'd been at the House of Commons lobby, was chairing the meeting. He wasn't known for being militant and we half expected a telling off. There were guys from the main engineering unions – AUEW, Electricians, as well as Boilermakers. There was one woman – Amanda Chorley from TSSA, who'd encouraged Midge when she was first getting involved in union affairs. Amanda was now deputy general secretary and had responsibility for BR Engineering. She was overjoyed to see Midge as part of the Horwich delegation.

"Midge! Great to see you! Give me a hug! I was expecting a load of blokes, asking me to go and make them cups of tea. When I saw 'M. Wrightson' on the attendance list I wondered if it might be you. And you're vice-chair of the Action Committee? Wonderful!"

"And 'councillor' as well!" Midge added.

"Fantastic! How do you manage to find the time?"

"Oh, I manage. The Council leadership make sure I don't get too much power."

"Tell me about it," replied Amanda. "Reactionary old blokes hate to see women getting involved and threatening their power. But they've had their day."

We sat down and shared the cups of tea. Around the room were portraits of previous general secretaries. All men, obviously, looking very neat and proper – wearing well-tailored suits with collar and tie, the older ones with watch-chains hanging down to their waistcoat pockets. There were photographs of past annual general meetings – 'Southend, 1919', Blackpool, 1931'...again, all blokes, until you got to 'Scarborough, 1963' when a couple of women attended. No black faces, though that was starting to change and some of the London and Manchester branches had sent black delegates to grades conferences and the last AGM.

Derek Shaw opened the meeting and welcomed us to Unity House.

"Thanks for coming along, brothers and sisters. And a very warm railway welcome to our engineering union colleagues. Let's do the introductions then get down to business."

We went quickly round the room introducing ourselves from Horwich, followed by Amanda from TSSA, Gavin Lord, the AUEW's full-time official responsible for the railway engineering membership, Jack Cox from the Electricians and Gordon Lewthwaite from the Boilermakers.

"Well brothers and sisters. The situation doesn't look good for railway engineering. BR is determined to slim-down production and concentrate on the big factories at Crewe, Derby and Glasgow. Swindon's under threat the same as Horwich. We've a loyalty to our membership as a whole and we don't want to jeopardise the future of Derby and Crewe. But I understand your feelings. I was on your march in London and was impressed by your determination and community support. So we want to support you, but winning this one isn't going to be easy."

"OK, I can understand where Derek's coming from," said Amanda. "All the railway workshops are struggling and Thatcher is gearing up to privatise BR Engineering. We need to be careful that we don't end up with even bigger job losses. But Horwich does have a case and we can't sacrifice 1,800 workers there without a fight."

"Aye, our members at Horwich hev nowhere left to go," said Gordon Lewthwaite, who'd served his time at Darlington North Road shops, only to see them close. "If they shut Horwich, I can see either Derby or Crewe closing. If we sit back and let them close Horwich, it'll only encourage them to wield the axe again. We've seen it all before."

Gavin Lord of the AUEW, which organised most of the workers at Horwich, responded. "Nobody wants to see Horwich close. A lot of the onus is on you guys. We don't have the support to take industrial action, neither in engineering nor, I think you'll agree Derek, on the railways. We will meet BR senior management and put the strongest possible case we can to save the Works but I don't hold out much hope. The best we can do is to get a good redundancy package and opportunities for redundant staff to transfer to other workshops. I know that's not what you want to hear."

"Aye, well no it's not, Gavin. We do have a plan and we want you to support us. We've got agreement on the Works Committee, and among the membership, to occupy the factory. Do a UCS. As soon as redundancy notices are issued, we take over. Take over the factory."

"And we've got support in the town as well. Political support, business support," added Midge. "Everyone is behind us, we're not giving up without a fight. If you don't support us, people will be asking why have they paid their union dues all these years?"

"Nobody's saying we won't support you sister," said Derek Shaw. "If you're willing to take direct action that's a decision for you and your members, as long as it remains lawful. We can treat it as official industrial action and give you strike pay. But I'm not sure what else we can do."

Midge had a ready answer. "If we take over the factory we're not going to sit down and play cards and sup tea all day. We want to carry on repairing wagons and carriages. Doing the work we've always done. We want you to get BR to continue dealing with us, supplying us with wagons, carriages and trains. And if push comes to shove, we'll run it ourselves as a co-operative."

Jack Cox, of the Electricians union, had stayed quiet so far. "I think it's a bloody good idea. I've been a member of the co-operative movement all my life and we've never really applied those principles to industrial production. What have these people got to lose? If they sit back the Works will close, they'll be out of a job and we'll see our union membership decline even more. Whether it's a short-term action to get BR to change its mind, or a long term strategy to take over and run the factory, we should be in there with them. I say we should urge BR to co-operate with the occupation, not penalise them."

Gordon Lewthwaite of the Boilermakers nodded in support. "We've only a handful of members left at Horwich," he said, but there have been members of the society at Horwich since it opened in 1885. If they think they can make a go of it, let's support them."

Derek Shaw moved to bring the meeting to a close. "We all need to go back to our executive committees and discuss this proposal. I can see my general secretary being less than enthusiastic about supporting anything that smacks of left-wing agitation so play down the CP influence won't you? You have my personal support, for what that's worth. But talk to your local NEC member Bill Fordham and make sure he's on side."

"Thanks Derek, thanks all of you," said Tommy. "You've given us the support we'd hoped for. We know you have to take this through your own democratic channels, as we've done with our members. We've been told on the quiet to expect the redundancy notices very soon so time's of the essence. You're all welcome to come up to Horwich, but by the time you do we may well be in occupation of the factory."

We left Unity House and went for a pub lunch down Euston Road. We'd arranged to meet Ernie Bowman, the CP's Industrial Organiser. He'd been a key figure at UCS, ensuring party-influenced unions and stewards' committees around the country were supportive. He had contacts in all of the CP-dominated unions in France, Italy and other parts of Europe. And he had friends in the Soviet Embassy. He was a combative but cheery Scot who'd been brought up in the engineering industry in Dundee. His dad had been a railwayman and one of the founders of the Communist Party in the city. Most of the family were communists, or left-Labour.

We debated the way forward over pints of bitter and plates of pie and chips. "If you occupy, the Party will back you all the way. We can get support from comrades in engineering, rail and mining. You're going to need money to keep going. There are mouths to feed. But one word of warning. This mustn't be a Communist Party campaign, any more than a Labour Party or SWP campaign. Keep your independence. If the press gets even a whiff that the Party is influencing the issue, you'll have lost."

"So what about all this Russian gold we keep hearing about? We could do with some of that!" Midge replied.

"If only..." said Ernie. "Things are changing in the Soviet Union under Gorbachev. They have no interest in interfering in other countries' internal politics. It's counter-productive in their view – and they're right. It's different even from strikes in the 1950s when Soviet trade unions were used as proxies for channelling Government money into a few strikes led by our comrades. "

The conversation turned to national politics. Thatcher was riding high in the polls after the Falklands War and there was talk of a snap general election. "Have you chosen a candidate yet for any Tory-held seats in the area?" asked Ernie. Thatcher might not be as popular as the polls suggest and the Loco Works issue might win Labour some votes."

"Well no," said Tommy, who was secretary of one of the branches of Westhoughton Constituency Labour Party. "It's been on our minds, and we don't want some wazzock from London being parachuted in. But we don't have anyone showing interest up here."

"What about you, Midge?" Ernie pointedly asked. "You're Labour aren't you? A councillor as well? Seems to me you'd make a great candidate, and the Party would support you, we've no interest in running candidates where a good Labour man – or woman – could unseat a Tory."

Midge coloured slightly – something I'd never seen her do before.

"That's a bloody good idea," Tommy got in quickly. "We need more women candidates and Midge is getting a high profile through the Works campaign and being a local councillor. She'd have as good a chance as any in beating that Tory, Simmons."

"Well he's a good supporter of our campaign," answered Midge. I'd feel really guilty standing against him, even if he is a Tory."

"Oh give over Midge," I said. "Don't be so sentimental. He's a Tory and he's propping up Thatcher. If we had a Labour MP in there it weakens the Tory grip on power. OK he's not a bad bloke but nothing's fair in love, war and politics."

"Well I'll think about it," Midge murmured. "I don't think I'm ready for it though."

On the train going home the conversation came back to the election and getting a good local candidate to fight the seat for Labour. Various names were banded about, none of whom were really up to much. Councillors, trade union officials, a couple of teachers who were active in the constituency party.

"Midge, you're our only hope!" said Tommy, as we pulled into Piccadilly station.

"And I agree," I chipped in.

19

December 10th 1982:   It starts

The redundancy notices arrived in the post that morning. Pretty much everyone on the payroll was being given notice to quit. The periods of notice varied according to 'length of service' but some of the poorest paid category 1 shopmen had just a month. Happy Christmas! The letter was couched with all sorts of caveats saying that there would be opportunities to transfer and this would be the subject of discussions with our personnel department. There was the usual management crap about what a caring employer they were, wanting to ensure the welfare of all their employees but how difficult decisions had to be made in the current climate. The letter said that production at the Works would cease completely by March 31st 1983, with the partial exception of the Foundry.

We were expecting it. And we were ready. By 9.30 a dozen of us had gathered at the Works gates.

We unfurled a huge banner and fastened it to the fencing. "NOW UNDER WORKERS CONTROL" said one. "Horwich Loco Works – Support The Occupation" said another.

How you 'occupy' a factory that you're already working in was a dilemma. Everyone was told to carry on working as normal. The main change was in the office. Tommy, Midge and some of the senior stewards knocked on George Barlow's door and were invited in. Cups of tea and biscuits were ordered.

"So you lads are in charge now," the Works Manager smiled. "You'll soon find out that running a big factory isn't as easy as it looks. So what do you want from me then?"

"Well Mr Barlow," said Tommy. "We hope you'll support us. Your wife Enid has been a great help on the Action Committee, but we know you are in a difficult position."

"You think so do you? Well let me show you this letter from BR Engineering Ltd's Director of Personnel, dated December 5th. It says *'Dear Mr Barlow, May I thank you for your 42 years of service with British Rail and British Rail Engineering Ltd. I am pleased to say that your request for early retirement has been agreed and you will cease to be employed by BREL with effect from December 31st 1982'.*"

So in a couple of weeks I'll be a free agent, drawing a nice pension with time for more golf and bird-watching. Unless anything else more interesting comes up."

"What, asked Midge. "Like being a director of Horwich Loco Workers' Co-operative?"

"Well that could be my idea of 'interesting'."

The next few days saw a few more changes to the usual pattern of life at Horwich. We put more banners alongside the Works fences and every lamp-post sprouted a 'Save Horwich Works' sign. We set up a modest 'hotel' in an unused part of the admin offices so that we'd have a continuous presence in the Works, with mostly single lads without family commitments. The 'no booze no sex' rule was rigorously enforced. If they wanted a shag or a pint there were plenty other places in Horwich they could go.

We converted the gatehouse into a reception centre where people could leave donations, food for the 'hotel' and messages of support. The old guys who worked there liked the extra company and carried on turning up for work in their uniforms. They acted as receptionists, media relations men and information advisors.

We took over the old board room, which had been out of use for years, as the campaign HQ and one of the typists – Julie - volunteered to act as admin support. Mrs Watson spent half her time in the Typing Pool and the rest writing up campaign leaflets and the newsletter. The first edition of 'Action for Horwich' was produced by the end of the week and sent to Pendlebury's, the local printers, to run off 2,500 copies. We distributed a thousand in the Works and the rest we took round the shops and pubs.

Things didn't look any different inside the factory. We still had a backlog of wagons, carriages and some electric trains for repair. We'd carry on fettling them until someone said 'stop'.

It was a sort of 'phoney war', giving us time to build up our own funds, get wider support and plan for the next stage of the campaign. We'd had offers of help from Tom Simmons' friends in the employers' federation and from academics in Manchester University.

In the second week of the occupation we got a phone call from the gatehouse to say we had a visitor. "She says as she's from Bolton Textile Employers Association and wants to see Tommy," said Fred, the duty gatekeeper.

"OK, send her down then," I told him. "Tommy's doing an interview with a chap from some Italian television company but he won't be long."

An elegant figure entered the campaign office, I'd say in her late 50s, blonde, nicely made-up but not too much. Her demeanour was slightly at odds with her broad Lancashire accent. She had a chihuaha dog in tow.

"Hello, I've been asked by my good friend Mr Tom Simmons MP that you might need a bit of help. I'm Gloria Tomlinson, secretary of the Bolton Textile Employers' Association. I'm not sure how I can help but here I am. Tell me to bugger off if I'm not of any use. And this is Rupert, my little pal."

"Well, very nice to meet you," said Midge, "and Rupert. We need all sorts of help, including a bit of commercial expertise. Business plans, marketing, possibly even running a company. But our chairman Tommy will be with us in a minute, we can have a proper chat then. Would you like a cup of tea?"

"Oh I'd love one if it's not too much trouble. And a bowl of water for Rupert please."

Tommy said goodbye to the journalist and walked into the committee room. He was surprised to see Mrs Tomlinson sat there with her cup of tea.

"By the 'ell, It's Gloria Shorrock isn't it?" Tommy exclaimed. "Ah were at school with you!"

"The same, except it's Gloria Tomlinson now, and has been for the last 35 years, though my husband – late husband, he always was - has been dead and buried for six years. I've been hearing about your campaign and Tom suggested I might be able to help you, if you need it...I only work part time for the association now – there aren't that many mills left in Bolton these days."

Gloria was co-opted onto the campaign committee. Her contacts with local employers came in handy, with no shortage of firms saying they'd always wanted to supply the Loco Works but could never find a way in through BR's arcane procurement rules which did no favours to small firms. We weren't in a position to start letting contracts – yet – but we knew where to go when we needed to.

She and Midge got on like a house on fire, even though Gloria was about as non-political as you could get. "Oh sometimes I vote Tory, sometimes Labour," she told Midge. "It depends on the candidate mostly. If they're any good – and local – they generally get my vote. But I do believe in justice and fair play."

In the Works Manager's office

A few days after we started the occupation I received a letter postmarked 'Lancaster'. It was from Simon.

"Dear Dave, I've got some bad news. My partner Michael died in hospital on December 5thth. The funeral was on Monday. He'd been diagnosed HIV Positive last year and had been in and out of hospital. The end came quite quickly and he wasn't in too much pain. I hope I gave him a lot of love, and I'll miss him. But it's exciting news about your occupation. It would take my mind off things if I could come down to help – whatever you want. I know you're shacked up with Midge and I won't get in the way. Won't be offended if it's too awkward. Best wishes, Simon"

The letter affected me more than my redundancy notice. I'd never got to meet Michael, and hadn't seen Simon since our drunken night in bed together. But I knew how much Michael meant to him and I couldn't stop crying when I put the letter down.

"Whatever's the matter love?" Midge asked. She knew about Simon, apart from the fact he'd nearly fucked me. "Well you must ask him to come down right away," she said. "I'll tidy up the spare bedroom. Let him stay as long as he wants."

Simon arrived with a rucksack full of clothes and books two days later. "I really don't want to be any trouble Dave, but I'll do anything to help with the occupation."

Midge had gone out to a Labour Party meeting in Westhoughton, a short bus ride away. The constituency party was holding a selection meeting and she was one of the three candidates. The others were from outside the area – one was leader of a local council in the West Midlands and the other was a lawyer from Manchester, who had been active on human rights issues.

The front door burst open just after 10.

"I'm the candidate!" shouted Midge. "Give me a hug!"

"Fantastic! Well done!" I give her a big bear hug and lifted her off her feet. "Oh and by the way, this is Simon..."

Simon gave her a warm handshake and offered his own congratulations.

"Has Dave been looking after you then, Simon? Have you had something to eat? I was so sorry to hear about your partner..."

"Well thanks, I'm not that hungry. Yes, he was a lovely guy and I miss him so much. It doesn't feel real yet to be honest. "

"Yes I know, it's an awful shock. I lost my husband in an accident years ago, completely unexpected. For weeks I kept expecting him back home for his tea. But anyroad, you're welcome here for as long as you want. Dave said you'd like to help with our little campaign? Well there's lots to do."

"Definitely. I'll do anything – delivering leaflets, brewing up, organising events....revolutions made to order."

The weeks before Christmas saw a few hundred of the older blokes leaving. They'd got their pensions and a lump sum for redundancy thrown in. They were happy, and a few of them made generous donations to the campaign fund, which now stood at £4,678.89. Gloria had taken over the job of Finance Director (unpaid), as she liked to be described - Midge was increasingly involved in meetings both about the Works campaign and for the Labour Party in Westhoughton.

The highlight of the festive season was the Christmas Party which we held in the Paint Shop. We cleared all the carriages out, using 'Percy' the Works shunting engine. It was already the cleanest place in the factory; paint shops had to be spotless. So we put down some carpets on the floor and trimmed the place up with decorations donated by the local shops. Some of the apprentices had formed their own band – 'The Horwich Loco Boys' – doing a mix of 60s cover versions, punk and R&B. They agreed to provide the musical entertainment. "But we don't want any of that punk rock stuff you're all into, OK?" said Midge.

About 300 turned up. There was a mountain of food, supplied by the local shops, ale and soft drinks from the RMI, Railway Club and other pubs and off-licences. It was free for works employees and we charged a couple of quid for anyone else, so we could raise a bit more cash for the fighting fund.

George and Enid Barlow turned up, both looking forward to his 'retirement'. We'd agreed that tonight wasn't about politics, or even the campaign. We were just out to have a good time and if we raised a bit of money, so much the better. George stood up and 'said a few words' before handing over to Adrian from the Machine Shop, who was tonight's DJ.

"Thanks everyone for turning out tonight, and to the lads of the Paint Shop for making their place into the No. 1 Horwich Night Club, for tonight at least. Next year will be exciting and demanding. As you know I retire from BREL next week and I've agreed to take on a new, unpaid, role as Director of Engineering – here at Horwich. You might ask what that means. I'm buggered if I do myself, but let's see what unfolds. Have a lovely evening and a merry Christmas – and a successful new year!"

The Foundry

We had laid the shop out with groups of tables that could seat 10 apiece. We had several special guests including councillors, the local clerics, other unions and our three MPs. Tom Simmons joined our table, together with Gloria and her latest boyfriend, a 20-something called Michael, Tom Gadsden the Methodist minister with his wife Joanne and Barbara Craddock one of the Horwich councillors who sat on Bolton Council with husband Bob. Vanessa was with her daughter Daisy.

It was a slightly cheeky move putting Midge on the same table as Tom, as they were both going to be fighting the same seat whenever the election was called. And some bright spark doing the table plan had sat them together.

"Well Midge – if you don't mind me calling you Midge," said the ever-polite Tom. "I hear you've been selected to fight Westhoughton Central for Labour? I'm pleased I've got a good local opponent, and I'm sure we'll treat each other with respect and fairness."

"Well thanks Tom – and of course you can call me Midge. Personally I wish I wasn't fighting you. You're far too nice and reasonable, and you're a great supporter of our campaign. But politics is politics. Let's fight a fair fight and may the best woman win!"

"Ha ha, I'll drink that Midge."

After the first course of the meal had been served we had the first round of music and song. Father O'Shaughnessy had a reputation for being a bit of a singer and he'd accepted a request to start the evening's entertainment. He began with some songs from his native country, including 'Forty Shades of Green' and 'The Minstrel Boy'. He then asked the lads from The Loco Boys to join him for some Presley numbers. 'Rock Around the Clock' became 'Rock Around the Shop' and some of the younger end got up and did a bit of jiving. Vanessa and daughter Daisy were first up.

The 'Loco Boys' proved a great hit and we put them down for touring round Lancashire to do fund raising concerts. We danced ourselves stupid and by the end of the night we were all well oiled too.

It had been a big help having Simon around. He stayed with us over Christmas and we got in plenty of walks up Rivington. He headed back to Lancaster after New Year.

"Keep in touch bonny lad," Midge called to him as he got on the bus.

20

January 1983:   The Police pay a visit

After the 'business as usual' of December things began to change when we came back. Those whose redundancy period was only four weeks got their severance payments in January. As we finished work on the wagons, carriages and trains that had been lined up since before the closure notice, the supply of new stock for repair began to dry up.

We pressed our union leadership about what was happening and they said they couldn't get BR to commit to the vague promises that they'd made before Christmas that they'd still send stock to Horwich. Midge had a chat with Amanda who suggested there was something going on behind the scenes that smelt of Government interference, but wasn't sure.

We started hearing noises that BR wanted to clear the Works and sell the site off to add insult to injury. A few right-wing Tory MPs started talking to the media about 'the rights of property' and asking why the police were standing by while the factory was occupied by 'a reckless bunch of Trotskyists'.

Our sole police presence was Jim Jolly who continued to call round for a brew, leaving his police-issue bike propped up by our banners proclaiming the Works being 'under workers' control.

"I'm glad to see everything is goin' peacefully," he said as he dunked a biscuit into his tea.

"Why shouldn't it Jim?" I asked.

"Well there's a few questions being asked at HQ about the leaders of your work-in – who they are, their politics an' that sort o' thing. Ah've towd 'em nowt, other than they're perfectly respectable members of the community. An' ah've said nowt about your politics David, but I got the impression they know already."

"Well it's a free country Jim – thanks for the information."

A week later, Jim's visits for a brew stopped, quite suddenly. We still saw him cycling past most days and he'd give a friendly wave. But no stopping off for a chat.

"Don't you think it's all a bit strange", I asked Midge, "that Jim Jolly has suddenly stopped his calls. And there was that speech from the chief constable last week about the threat posed by left-wing 'infiltrators' in industry? Am I adding two and two and making five?"

"I've had the same thoughts," Midge replied. Something's going on. I think we should strengthen the picket on the gate but re-iterate the point that this is a peaceful work-in."

It was a freezing Tuesday night in the middle of January when the attack came. A handful of lads were on security duty at the gates while another ten or twelve were kipped down in the gatehouse. As a precaution we'd increased the presence in each of the shops, following our precautionary discussions the previous week. But not just that. We had a note pushed through the gatehouse letterbox the previous night saying "Be on your guard."

It all seemed very cloak and dagger. I'd mentioned it to Tommy Handley and he poo-poo'd the idea that there would be an attempt by anyone – BR or the Police – to break the occupation.

"We've been entirely peaceful," Tommy argued. "Nothing has been damaged. Productivity has actually gone up in some shops. Imagine the negative publicity if they tried to smash us? Who'd be that stupid?"

My unease wasn't eased when on the Monday evening news the Tory Home Affairs minister made a speech condemning 'communist infiltrators' and specifically mentioned "the illegal occupation at Horwich Railway Works."

It was 2.00 a.m. on Tuesday morning when the police vans arrived. About twenty of them, with sirens screaming and lights blazing, screeched to a halt outside outside the gates. We'd taken the precaution of padlocking them. The coppers who streamed out of the vans wore helmets and carried riot shields with truncheons drawn. Not your kindly old copper stopping off for a brew. These were big tough guys who looked like they wanted a riot to quell.

A copper, obviously in charge, appeared at the Gatehouse, with his cronies lined up behind him.

"I'm Superintendent Millward of Greater Manchester Police, Tactical Aid Group. I am under orders to take control of this property which is illegally occupied. I must ask you to open the gates and allow us to gain entry."

"Show us your authority then," asked Tommy, stepping forward. "We are running a wholly peaceful operation to defend our jobs and have the backing of our MPs, the churches and everyone in this town."

The film crew we'd asked to join us appeared. They were from a Manchester co-op who'd been doing a documentary about the occupation. Following the tip-off we told them they might get something a bit more dramatic if they didn't mind an overnight stay. The presence of the film crew clearly un-nerved the senior copper but he was determined to 'obey his orders.'

"Open the gates or we'll force them open," he barked. "And stop those cameras."

By this time half of Horwich was awake and a large crowd had started to gather at the gates.

"Hands off Horwich! Hands off Horwich!" the cry went up, from the assembled throng of men, women and quite a few kids as well.

The first police van reversed into the road and took a run at the gates. The iron buckled but didn't break. The van reversed to have another attempt. Meanwhile the cameras were still rolling and the crowd had swelled even more. About 30 women – including some of the Typing Pool - stood in front of the gates.

"If you don't move you'll be arrested!" Millward yelled.

"Go then, arrest us!" young Sonia screamed. She'd come a long way since my last encounter with her and had been elected office rep the previous month.

The next arrival was Father O'Shaughnessy.

"May I speak to the officer in charge here?"

Millward came up to him and informed the priest that he was obeying his orders to end an illegal occupation. "Half of these people are communists who'd have you shot" he told O'Shaughnessy, as the cameras continued to roll.

"Officer, seize that camera!" He instructed one of his helmeted men.

After that, hell broke loose as the camera crew resisted having their equipment taken and the rest of the crowd dived in to help them. The riot squad began hitting out at the crowd, and little Sonia got a nasty whack on the head. There was a lot of blood. Some of the young lads from the Smithy had brought their tools and started to defend themselves. Bricks and lumps of coal were thrown towards the police lines. A large tub of 4" steel nuts from the Smithy, known as 'Horwich Confetti', was placed close to the gates.

More people from the surrounding streets arrived, shouting abuse at the police. Eggs were thrown. Within seconds it was a pitched battle with vastly outnumbered, but heavily armed, police forced onto the defensive. The fighting became more vicious with several of the coppers retreating back to their vans, nursing knock-out blows from the Smithy battalion. A hail of confetti descended on the retreating cops, only partly protected by their riot shields.

A moment later a solitary uniformed figure arrived at the gatehouse on his bike. PC Jolly rested his bike by the gatehouse and approached Millward, who was dodging a hail of bricks and coal.

"What the fucking hell are you lot doing here? I've been keeping an eye on these lads for weeks and they've not done owt wrong. This is my patch and it's you fuckers who are trespassing. With all due respect, piss off, the lot of you!"

"Listen officer," said Millward, "we're the Tactical Aid Group and our orders are to take back control of this factory. You're just some local plod who is exceeding his authority. We're going in, get out of our way."

By this time the crowd must have been 500 or more. The film crew, having managed to save most of their equipment, continued filming the confrontation.

The van was about to make a further attempt to force the gates when a familiar-looking looking Jaguar stopped by the embattled gates, preventing further assaults. It was George Barlow, the Works Manager.

"I don't care what authority you claim to have, I am the Works Manager, appointed by the British Railways Board. I'm in charge here and I'm telling you to withdraw. Now." The next minute a baton came down on the back of his head, knocking him senseless. This led to renewed assaults on the police lines by the emboldened lads – and quite a few lasses – who had learnt the art of insurrection remarkably quickly.

I felt a tap on my shoulder and turned round to see Paddy Doherty – whose house we'd bought. "Well that's a surprise! What are you doing up here?"

"Well I came up for a funeral and to see a few old mates. I didn't expect this to blow up – it reminds me of The Bogside in August '69. We beat the B-Specials then and we'll beat this lot. Would you be needing any advice on how to make petrol bombs?"

"Well thanks Paddy but that won't be necessary. I think we've got them on the run anyway."

More coppers retreated back to their vans. It was clear that they were losing control of the situation though some were still lashing out with their batons in a rearguard battle against overwhelming force.

A black unmarked car appeared and a uniformed copper emerged, with a strong look of authority about him. He approached Millward, who deferred to his obvious superior. "Can we have a quiet word officer?"

Within two minutes the coppers were back in their vans and drove off, at speed, down Chorley New Road to cheers from the crowd and a few more 4" nuts to speed them on their way.

"I should book the buggers for speeding," said PC Jolly. "Coming here and behaving like that. Disgraceful. Now can I ask everyone to disperse please. Hasta no whums fert goo to?"

At which point PC Jolly, approaching retirement after 40 years unblemished service in the Lancashire and Greater Manchester Constabularies, received a huge round of applause from the crowd.

The following day, 'The Siege of Horwich Loco Works' was on every news channel - across the UK, Europe and the States. The hero of the hour was PC Jolly, filmed confronting his superior officer, fortunately without the sound effects. The scenes of riot police lashing out with their truncheons at teenage girls didn't exactly go down well with TV viewers, nor for that matter with the Tory MP, who demanded an explanation from the Home Office Minister as to what was going on at Horwich.

Sacks of letters of support began to arrive at the Gatehouse, many with cheques and cash.

"We should thank that copper, Millward," Tommy told the special meeting of the Works Committee. He's given us more positive publicity than we could ever dream of. Here's to the Tactical Aid Group!"

A week later it was announced that Chief Superintendent Millward had taken early retirement 'on health grounds'. Police Constable Joe Jolly was approaching retirement and he agreed to take the honorary title of 'security advisor' to the workers' co-operative.

21

March 1983: The polite civil servant

After the failure of the attempt to break the occupation, the mood in the factory was exultant. But there was a shadow looming: the lack of any new work coming in. Since January not a single repair job arrived, neither wagons nor coaches. Yet we knew that Derby and Crewe couldn't handle the demand for repairs that we were kitted out to do.

It was agreed that Midge would make a few discreet enquiries. She rang Tom Simmons' office to see if the MP was around. "Sorry, Mr Simmons is busy but he'll ring you back."

Tom rang back himself within 20 minutes. "Hello Midge. How can I help?"

"Well Tom, we're trying to find out what's going on with BR. We've stopped receiving new rolling stock for repair and there's a suggestion that your Government might be putting pressure on them to starve us out, effectively. Especially after the fiasco in January with the police."

"Well I'll see what I can find out. It's news to me but I'm not even a junior minister, so I don't get to find out what's happening a lot of the time. And you do know the police action had nothing to do with me. It was outrageous."

"I believe you Tom but it came from somewhere in your Government. But let's draw a veil over that for now. We need you to help us get some work into the factory."

He was as good as his word and rang back two days later. He said he'd done his best to help - but admitted couldn't get to the bottom of what was going on. "I've tried ringing BREL management as well as sounding out our own people, but nobody's saying anything. Sorry Midge. I'll keep trying."

Three days later, on a Monday morning, a taxi turned up at the gates. A youngish chap in a grey pin-striped suit, with a bulging briefcase, stepped out. He arrived at the gatehouse and asked to speak to 'Mr Hindley' – if that was possible. "Oh aye, an' who shall ah say is askin'?" enquired Billy Hargreaves, one of the elderly watchmen.

"Mr Lionel Worthington, from the Ministry of Transport."

"Oh aye. Well sit thisel deawn an' ah'll see if he's free."

"Tommy? There's some posh bloke at the gatehouse as says he wants to see thi'. Lionel Worthington ah think he said, Ministry of Transport. Hasta not taxed thi car?"

A few minutes Tommy appeared at the gatehouse.

"Mr Worthington? We didn't know about you coming. How can we help?"

"I'm very sorry to turn up unannounced Mr Hindley. Perhaps we could go and talk somewhere a bit more private?"

"Yes, of course, but I'd like to have our Works Manager with me as well if it's a serious matter."

"Well, yes, it is – and he'd be very welcome to join in the conversation but I must ask that it is kept strictly confidential."

Worthington explained that he was a senior civil servant in the Ministry, with responsibilities for policy, particularly in the rail engineering sector. He had been asked to come up to Horwich by his minister to explore 'possibilities for co-operation', in the wake of the recent 'unfortunate incident' as he described the police attack.

They sat down in George's office and he asked Jane, his newly-recruited

PA, to arrange tea and biscuits.

"Mr Hindley and Mr Barlow, let me come straight to the point. The Government wants to support any genuine attempt to maintain production at Horwich and we applaud your efforts. However, there is a political dimension to all this as I'm sure you are aware and we cannot be seen to be encouraging militancy or illegal occupations."

"Well let me assure you, Mr Worthington, we are not doing anything that we regard as illegal and we're here with the consent – or at least acceptance - of the British Railways Board. But if we are 'militants' in wanting to protect our jobs, and those of our sons and daughters, well so be it, we plead guilty as charged," responded Tommy.

"Yes, I fully appreciate that Mr Hindley, I really do. And you have the support of your local members of parliament, including a member of this Government, as I'm sure you are aware."

"Well we hope so, responded George. "But why was the Tactical Aid Group sent to break the occupation, might we ask? They obviously had support from a high level."

"Yes, I understand your question and your concerns. Can I say between us that there are some elements within Government which are not always fully answerable to due process. The unfortunate incident was not sanctioned by the Ministry and we abhorred the tactics used by the police that night. I think we can all agree that their intervention was deeply unhelpful and I very much regret the injuries that occurred. Partly, that is why I'm here. The Ministry would like to explore ways – strictly off the record please – in which train building can be encouraged at Horwich. And I should add that this is something I feel very deeply about on a personal level, being from the area, originally."

"Well that's good to hear Mr Worthington and we appreciate your honesty. What we want is very simple. We want BR to co-operate with us by sending work – carriages and wagons for repair, on-going contracts that give us stability and steady growth. We know the work is there, we know there are trains stuck in sidings that should be in service but need overhaul. BR has closed down so many of its engineering works that the capacity isn't there to meet current demand, let alone any future growth," replied Tommy.

"Yes I fully understand that Mr Hindley. But the Government cannot be seen to be instructing BR to change its current policy on repairs. That is a matter for BR and British Rail Engineering Ltd. But sometimes influence can be exerted, in subtle ways. What we do not want is any of this to get out into the press. We must not be seen to be giving in to extremism. The Minister feels particularly strongly about this."

"So I think I get the gist of what you're saying Mr Worthington. It is that your Minister wants to be seen to be supporting what we're doing but not too directly? That it's up to BR to offer us repairs if there is a commercial need for them to do so?" asked George.

"Yes, that's precisely the situation. I'm sorry I cannot be more specific."

It was left to Tommy to lighten the tone. "So you're a Bolton lad then, Mr Worthington?"

"Yes, Great Lever. My father worked in local government. Lower middle class, he and mum were children of cotton workers. Dad was in the army during the war and got rapid promotion within the Council after 1945. I used to like watching the steam trains rattle through Bolton station, perhaps that's where my interest in railways came from. I went to Oxford and ended up as a civil servant in the Ministry of Transport."

"So a Bolton lad then," said Tommy. "But you've lost your accent haven't you? I'd have had you down for a southerner!"

"Well, I never really had much of an accent. Prep school made sure of that, followed by grammar school. When I came home to Bolton mum and dad would almost treat me as a visiting dignitary, bringing out the best crockery. So my visits became less and less, we all felt too awkward. I came out with a first at Oxford and got fast-tracked into the Civil Service, but felt I'd lost my roots."

"So much for our wonderful class system, eh Mr Worthington?" Tommy responded. "But we can all do our bit. What we're asking from you is to help us unlock some goodwill in BR and get us back in production."

"I can't commit to anything, as I'm sure you will understand. Let me see what can be done and please, keep this conversation to ourselves."

"We're men of our word Mr Worthington, don't worry about that. And I hope you will do all that you can to help us."

"Good day, gentlemen. Perhaps someone could ring a taxi for me to Bolton station?"

Two weeks later we got a phone call from Jack Harwood, signalman at Blackrod Junction and one of the NUR delegates to the Trades Council. "I've just had a special traffic notice. You've got two trains coming in this week – one's empty coaching stock from Willesden. The other's empty wagons from Healey Mills, in Yorkshire. Looks like someone's turned the tap back on for you!"

Seeing the first train arrive, with a diesel loco dragging 16 carriages looking in need of some TLC, was a sight to gladden a lot of Horwich hearts. They creaked and groaned up the branch from Blackrod, hauled by a mucky diesel.

A Southern Region electric train in the Works yard, ready for overhaul

"It's like the arrival of the Seventh Cavalry!" said George North, foreman at the Erecting Shop. "Or the Relief of Mafeking," said Ezra Lord as the assemblage came to a stand in the Works yard.

"Shall we leave 'em here then?" asked the Preston driver who'd brought the train up from Crewe. "Oh aye, said Tommy as he surveyed the carriages. "We'll get Percy to come an' shunt 'em wheer we want 'em."

The carriages were in a mess. Not your average vehicles in need of a bit of a refresh, but major surgery required. "They've sent us a right bag of shit here, haven't they?" said George Barlow, a man seldom given to expletives.

"Well we've no choice but to turn 'em out in gradely fettle, an' hope they send us mooar stuff," said Tommy.

The process of overhauling a railway carriage is lengthy, involving stripping it down to its component parts. The body is lifted off and anything that's rotten gets disposed of. The main thing is getting the frame and wheels checked to ensure they're in reasonable order and no sign of decay. Wheels can be changed but the frame can be a bigger problem. The carriage that would go into the works will come out as a different vehicle, in many cases. New or different sets of wheels, major bodywork, new or refurbished seats and a full repaint.

We made a start on them. But would they be a 'one off'?

22

March 1983:   Horwich Engineering is born

We never quite got to the bottom of how the tap was turned back on but we suspected 'Mr Worthington' had played a part. Tom had done some lobbying among his Government colleagues – the junior transport minister was an old friend whom he'd been at Oxford with. And the unions had been putting pressure on BREL, suggesting that they could have an all-out strike in the workshops if those plucky chaps at Horwich were being seen to be punished, especially after the ham-fisted police attempt to smash the occupation. Feelings were running high and there were resolutions coming up at the union AGM calling for strike action against workshop closures.

We all knew that the present arrangement with the work-in couldn't last. BREL was hoping we'd lose interest when the weekly wage packets stopped. The men would drift off and find jobs elsewhere. They were showing no sign of wanting to keep anything at Horwich apart from a few dozen workers repairing brake blocks in the foundry. A concession, so they said, to total closure. The rest of the factory site would be sold off.

Who would be daft enough to buy it? Well, we would, if we could get a package together. The problem was, we didn't know whom we were negotiating with. The British Railways Board? BR Engineering, its subsidiary? Or the Government? George Barlow did some investigating for us.

It was BR Engineering in Derby who was in charge of our fate, at least on paper. They'd been tasked with running us down and possibly finding a buyer, either for the Works as a going concern, or for the land that could go for housing. George knew a lot of the guys at Derby – he'd served his time there and he had a few favours to pull in. But what he was asking for was ambitious, if not utopian. George put the proposal to an 'explanatory' meeting with some of his former colleagues at Derby.

"We want you to give us the Works, the site and the assets. Peppercorn rent, and then let's discuss purchase when we're on our feet." "Well, you're not asking much then," one of George's colleagues responded. "We'll have a think."

"Well if we don't ask we won't get," later argued George in a Works Committee meeting. "BR isn't going to carry on sending us carriages and wagons to repair. The stuff they've sent would normally just go for scrap. They're playing games to show they're doing something - to please ministers. I've spoken to some of my old mates at Derby and there might be a way forward. It means we set up our own company and start trading with BREL as a supplier. They can't guarantee how much they could give us and their first priority would be their own remaining workshops – Derby, Crewe and Glasgow. But we would have freedom to tender for other engineering work, in the UK and abroad.

Gloria was enthusiastic. "Wasn't that what you wanted in the first place? For the workers to run the factory as a co-op? Look, you've shown you can run the place, let's take the next step and get ourselves formed as a trading company."

We had no shortage of good advice. Gloria had her own contacts and some of the academics at Manchester Business School helped us too. The Co-operative Trust in Manchester came down and talked us through how we set up a workers' co-operative. It wasn't as complicated as we thought.

We spent most time arguing about a name. Some nostalgists wanted 'Lancashire and Yorkshire Railway Engineering', as a reference to the original company who set up the Works. Others thought 'Horwich

Railway Engineering' was better.

In the end it was Midge who came up with the winner. "How about 'Horwich Engineering' then? It's simple, it trades on our world-wide reputation and it doesn't tie us down to railway engineering. We can diversify, if it makes sense to."

We called a special meeting to set up the company. We appointed ten directors – George Barlow, Gloria, Midge, Tommy, myself and five others from the different shops, to be going on with. We'd set up as an Industrial and Provident Society and all members of the workforce could become members. We would operate on classic co-operative principles of 'one member one vote'. George was promoted to 'managing director.' Unpaid.

We needed capital. The Action Committee funds were just a few thousand. We needed millions to run the business and it was hard to imagine most banks funding some lefty workers' co-operative up North in a place called Horwich. But we got support from unexpected sources. Tom Simmons had friends who were big in finance. They offered to underpin the new business. The National Union of Railwaymen offered an interest-free loan to match it.

BREL, thanks to George's contacts, said they'd be willing to lease the Works site to us, initially on a peppercorn rent basis for two years, after which it would be reviewed. Risky, but we didn't have any option.

Horwich Engineering Ltd (sub-titled 'a workers' co-operative') was born, on March 1st 1983. We had a workforce of just under a thousand. Many of the workers had taken early retirement or redundancy. It wasn't an ideal mix – we were over-staffed in some areas and under-resourced in others. We had to break down some of the old demarcations and get more flexibility. We were already talking like capitalists. But at least we were our own capitalists.

We organised a reception at the Works to mark the event and Horwich Band was recruited to play. The three MPs, council leaders, some of the union leaders and big shots from BR and BREL came along. *The Bolton Evening News* ran the headline 'Red Letter Day for Horwich.'

But behind all the handshakes and bonhomie, we knew we had a huge struggle ahead. Most of us had not been paid for over a month and bills were mounting up. If our co-op was going to succeed it had to pay its workers and that meant having an income. We couldn't afford to lose our skilled workers but we couldn't blame them for starting to look at jobs coming up elsewhere. British Leyland was said to be taking on skilled men and it was only a short drive from Chorley, where many of our guys lived.

We didn't have any firm orders from BR. We used the launch to do a bit of informal lobbying, mainly through George's contacts who came along from BREL and BR.

It turned out that Merseyrail had several trains that needed major overhaul and they'd been sat in the depot at Kirkdale for months, waiting to have work done. If we could get them fixed in three months, they'd grab our hands off.

The four sets of electric trains arrived a couple of weeks later. They were in better shape than the Southern trains that had arrived earlier. We got the contracts drafted and signed as we were stripping the carriages down. The deal was 'we'll do the job, you pay us as soon as the sets get sent back to depot'.

In the meantime, we had no choice but to pay the remaining 950 staff out of the loans we'd got. Once the income started flowing we'd put the money back into the capital fund. It was very high risk. Could we do anything else?

The Scrapyard

23

April 1983: The General Election

"Thatcher calls General Election for June 9th." *The Bolton Evening News* headline met the day shift coming out of the Works.

It wasn't unexpected, though Thatcher could have carried on for another year if she'd wanted. But she was still popular after the jingoism of the Falklands War and the economy was showing some signs of recovery.

The two Labour seats were regarded as safe enough but Labour Party national office – Transport House – didn't regard the Tory-held Westhoughton Central as being winnable in the current climate. The candidate – our Midge - wasn't a member of the party clique and there were suspicions she was too close to the Communist Party, like when she was adopted as a council candidate. The message coming up from London was 'you're on your own'.

Midge put together a strong team of local activists, with Ken Arkwright agreeing to act as her agent. He was an astute political operator – a retired maths teacher who loved collecting and analysing data. But more than a number cruncher, a dedicated socialist whose hero was Nye Bevan.

At the first meeting of the campaign committee he outlined the challenge.

"It's like this. The Tories have a majority of just over 5,000 with a reasonably popular MP, Tom Simmons. He's been careful to be seen supporting the Loco Works campaign and he's always distanced himself from Thatcher. He's a classic 'one nation' Tory. He's 'old money' and was born with a spoon in his mouth. That's a potential weakness we could exploit. But our biggest problem is the Social Democrats. They could easily split the Labour vote and ensure Simmons gets in, even though their candidate is a councillor in Surrey whom no-one has heard of. The chances of us winning are slim - but we must not rule it out. People are worried about their jobs with the Loco Works situation and the 'Falklands Factor' might not be as strong as we think. We need to get our own vote out in our strongholds – the council estates and terraces – but we have to go out into the new private housing and eat into the Tory support. If we're serious about having a chance of winning, we've got to be out every day, morning noon and night. And we need to try and get some big hitters to speak in the constituency, even though Transport House has written us off."

"Well thanks Ken," Midge responded. "That's an excellent summary. But I'll say this. If you want me for your candidate I'm not going to indulge in any personal attacks on Simmons. I think it would be counter-productive, as well as unethical. We run a principled fight that concentrates on the issues – jobs, housing, schools – and if we don't win on that basis, at least we can hold our heads high."

There was a debate about whether to exploit Simmons' wealthy background, with Joe Leather, one of our few local Militant Tendency supporters, wanting a hard-hitting 'class against class' attack. "He might be all smiles and smoothness but he's part of a viciously reactionary Tory Government," he argued. "We should expose his class privilege and appeal to the workers' class consciousness."

"Well I have to say I think Midge is right," said Ken Arkwright. "On balance, we could end up losing rather than gaining support if we went for personal attacks on Simmons. This isn't a radical left-wing constituency. People vote Labour out of habit, because that's what their parents did. They aren't class warriors."

The feel of the meeting was to support Midge's line and concentrate on the big local issues. Her involvement in the Loco Works was a major plus, and her face had been a regular feature in *The Bolton Evening News* and *Westhoughton Journal* for months.

There was no debate within the Communist Party about support for Midge. If anyone had suggested we put a candidate up against her they'd have got short shrift not just from me but from most of the other comrades. So the collective might of Horwich and Westhoughton branch of The Communist Party of Great Britain swung behind the Labour Party campaign. All twelve of us. The bourgeoisie must have been trembling.

But we did make a difference. We had several retired members, like Jim Lee, who could spend all hours addressing envelopes, knocking on doors or delivering leaflets. We were helped with fine weather. We didn't get much help from the Labour Party head office, but we hadn't expected it. The best they could do was send up some MP from Portsmouth whom nobody had heard of. Through Midge's union pals in London we got some left-wing Labour MPs, including a recently-elected young firebrand called Jeremy Corbyn, to come up and speak. I couldn't help thinking that if they were all like him, why bother having a Communist Party? But they weren't. And the guy from Portsmouth was useless, managing to lose us a few votes by starting off saying how wonderful it was to be here in 'Yorkshire'.

Midge devoted her heart and soul to the campaign, holding open-air meetings all round the constituency, going into community centres, pubs and cafes with the Labour message. She even managed to get into *The Sun* as 'Militant Midge', over her demand to abandon nuclear weapons. She got told off by Transport House because it wasn't party policy. "Tell them to fuck off," I advised her. "Already have done love."

A week before the election Ken spoke to the campaign committee. "The responses we're getting on the doorstep are good. Very good. You always get people exaggerating their support, and sometimes not bothering to vote, or changing their minds in the voting booth. But we need to really crank up the campaign in the last few days and make sure we get the vote out on polling day."

By June 9th we were knackered. We'd fought a strong campaign, leafleted the whole constituency at least twice and knocked on every single door. That didn't mean we'd talked to everyone – sometimes people ignored the knock, knowing it was 'them fuckin' politicians', but as Ken had sensed, the response on the doorstep was pretty positive.

Tom Simmons fought a slick, well-resourced campaign. The Tories, sensing possible trouble over the Loco Works issue, shipped in dozens of activists from around the North – and beyond – to support their man. Their leaflets stressed Simmons' support for the Loco Works campaign and his local record, minimising mention of Thatcher, who was hated by many in the area.

The ballots were to be counted in Bolton Town Hall and we were told that it could be as late as 5 in the morning before there'd be a result. So we spent the last few hours of the campaign running round like blue-arsed flies, getting the lazy sods to vote who said they'd support us. Again, Ken's mastery of the 'Reading System' where we checked people going into vote against canvass returns was invaluable. By 9.00 we knew which of our supporters still hadn't been down to the polling station. It was rewarding as well as annoying when you got people saying "Oh aye lad, just bin watchin' th'telly, ah'll get deawn theer reet away." To which we said "Well you've got 20 minutes – let's give you a lift down in the car," almost dragging them out of the house.

When polling stations closed we headed for The Red Lion. There was a good camaraderie between the campaign team, which had a sizeable CP influence in it. Even some of the more right-wing Labourites recognised we'd done more than our fair share. Midge was effusive: "Well you commies have done a grand job, our Dave," she said, giving me a hug as I reached for our pints at the bar. "How do you fancy being an MP's partner?"

I must say it didn't appeal to me at all, and I didn't want to lose Midge from the Works campaign, which was far from won. But I said "Well Midge, you know I like carrying your bags – and we can get a nice flat in London."

We got down to Bolton Town Hall just after midnight. Some members of the campaign team were already at the count, scrutinising the ballot papers. Simmons arrived a few minutes after we'd got there, looking more than a bit worried.

"Well hello Midge, it's good to see you – and yourself David. Thanks for the way you've fought the campaign, it's been very civilised." I felt like saying that that was more than could be said for some of the things his Government had been doing, but resisted.

As the votes were counted, our feelings went up and down. A large pile of voting papers for Midge in the working class wards were off-set by strong Tory support in other more middle class areas. "It's not exactly neck-and-neck," said Ken, "though we're not doing bad. But I'm worried by the votes that the SDP are getting in some of our areas."

At 5.25 a.m. the Returning Officer – Ray Southgate, the chief executive of the council, asked the candidates to come up to the stage.

"Ladies and gentlemen, as the Returning Officer for the Westhoughton Central Constituency, it is my duty to announce the voting as follows:

Martin Walshaw – Social Democratic Party – 7,320 votes

Mrs Marjorie Wrightson, Labour Party, 18,579 votes

Mr Thomas Simmons, Conservative and Unionist Party, 19,432 votes

I therefore declare Mr Thomas Simmons duly elected."

The Tory supporters were overjoyed. But we all knew Midge would have walked it, had it been a straight fight between Labour and Tory. We'd hardly seen anything of Walshaw throughout the campaign but the national media had been pushing the breakaway SDP for all it was worth. Midge went over to Simmons and gave him a friendly hand-shake and he responded by giving her a slightly more than friendly kiss on the lips. Cheeky bugger, but I pretended not to see.

Walshaw shook hands with the other two candidates and slunk off back down south to wherever he'd come from, never to be seen again. Thanks pal, I guiltily but sincerely thought.

I took Midge home, thinking I could make it up to her with a bit of fun and games. But as soon as we hit the bed we were dead to the world. Power had eluded Midge, and I was happy.

24

June 1983:   Dreams and dilemmas

Thatcher got back in. Labour was in disarray and she was able to capitalise on the war patriotism she'd worked up over the Falklands. What a nation of numpties we'd become. So we'd another five years of Thatcher to look forward to. Bye bye northern manufacturing. It was on its knees already, with mills and factories closing left right and bloody centre. But who was bothered, as long as the Union Jack was flying over a load of fucking penguins?

It was back to business as usual with the Loco Works campaign. We were all relieved in a way - we could now get on with the job of creating our little island of workers' co-operation here in Horwich.

I thought Midge might've taken it worse than she did. She'd plenty to keep her busy at the Works, and she was now a company director. Then there was her council work, which plodded along. We woke up at about 11.00 on Friday morning after the election result and I made her a cup of tea.

"Get that down you Midge, then let's snuggle up in bed for an hour before we go down to the Works.

"Thanks love. Bloody hell, is that the time? We said we'd have a meeting of the company board at 1.00. We'd better shape."

"Oh give over, you deserve a bit of a rest. They won't be expecting you there on the dot."

"Maybe not but punctuality is one of my watchwords, as you well know. Pity it hasn't rubbed off on you."

"Just put that cup of tea down and give us a kiss..."

"Men! You're all the same, only after one thing – sex. Billy was just the same, though you and him are about as different as chalk and cheese in every other way."

"Oh come on Midge, get off your high horse and relax....."

"Oh I suppose so...a few minutes late won't do any harm, will it?"

We got down to the Works for about 1.45 which wasn't bad. And the sex was bloody good. We must have looked a bit dishevelled when we walked into the room. We didn't expect what came next.

There were about 25 people sat round the boardroom table and everyone went quiet when we came in. Without any prompting they all stood up and clapped. They then started with "For she's a jolly good fellow..."

One thing Midge always used to run a mile from was any sort of praise or recognition. I had to grab hold of her to stop her running out of the room – I could tell she was near to tears. "Get back in there Midge, they're your mates!"

"I know, but it's just too much, I can't handle it..."

We came back in and everyone was still on their feet. Tommy was first to speak.

"Midge, you fought a brilliant campaign. We're proud of you. There'll be other opportunities, I'm sure of that. Thatcher won't last for ever. And besides, we've a business to run and we need you here in Horwich, not down in London. Oh, and we've got you these."

Tommy stooped down under the table and brought out a bunch of flowers – a nice mix of colours, mainly yellow and purple representing the suffragettes.

"Oh thanks so much Tommy, and all of you. Thanks so much for your support during the campaign. And thanks to my fella, Dave, for all your support. Don't let it go to your head, but you've been fantastic." OK, it was my turn to blush. We gave each other a comradely kiss and sat down.

"Right then," announced Tommy. "Let's get back to business then. Can we move on to the Finance Director's report please. Gloria? Oh, sorry, Mrs Tomlinson."

"Thanks Tommy, and Gloria's perfectly acceptable, we don't need to be too formal do we? Right then, I've circulated my report and it's starting to look encouraging.... But – there's no room at all for complacency. A few orders from Merseyrail isn't going to guarantee our future. But they were pleased with the quality of our work on those electric trains, and we met their deadline, just. We've got four more sets coming in for overhaul next month. That's worth about £100,000 to us. But don't get too excited, we've some difficult decisions to make. Which is why George wants to say something, as MD."

Tommy asked everyone to approve the financial report and turned to George Barlow.

"George, you've something to tell us then?"

"Well, yes Tommy I have. As you all know we've been looking at the size – and shape – of the workforce. A lot of men took redundancy when BREL pulled out. That helped us in some ways though we lost some skills which we've had to buy in from elsewhere. But we're still top heavy in some areas. The Paint Shop and Erecting Shop are both over-manned and we probably have a few too many in the offices as well. Modern technology means we don't need so many typists – or draughtsmen. The reality, if we're to survive as a viable business, is that we need to shed staff. Probably at least 150."

You could sense the tension in the room. Archie Johnston stood up first. He was trembling.

"Mister Chairman. Have we created this workers' co-operative just to be able to act like any other capitalist outfit by sacking workers? Is that what all the sacrifice was for? It's a very sad day for Horwich if we've got to announce redundancies. We can't go down that road."

Gloria was quickly on her feet.

"Mr Chairman and colleagues. I understand Archie's anger. It's very, very difficult. But if we don't make some very hard decisions now, we could end up having to close down completely in twelve months. Whether we're a workers' co-op or some old family firm like I knew in textiles, we're in a competitive market and no-one's going to do us any favours. We can create a viable business but we've got to have a workforce that matches our requirements, and we also need to invest in new equipment so we can make the best of our skilled colleagues – who at the end of the day, are our masters."

Jim Jackson, the HR director whom we'd poached from Shildon, stood up and outlined where we needed to make reductions, but also where we needed to strengthen the workforce.

"As Gloria has pointed out, we're overmanned in several departments and we need to offer a voluntary redundancy package. In some cases we can offer a re-training programme. Some of the men we've got on our books did their apprenticeships in the days of steam. Nobody's building steam locomotives now and we don't need boilermakers nor coppersmiths. But we need workers who're skilled in computer design and modern traction equipment. And we need to modernise the office and install new IT equipment – and throw those old typewriters onto the scrapheap."

I didn't say much in the debate, and neither did Midge. We weren't involved in this campaign to make people redundant. It was anathema to us. But I could understand what George and Gloria were saying. So this was the reality of running your own factory, of workers' control. I wondered what the party would make of it? There was a branch meeting next week so I'd have to raise the issue, though I was pretty sure some of the old guard would do anyway. I was in for a rough ride.

The discussion went on for another three quarters of an hour and the decision of the board was to offer a package of voluntary redundancy to particular parts of the workforce. We'd enter into discussions with the unions immediately, though many of the union reps – like myself - were now board directors, so they understood the situation.

"Well thank you colleagues," said Tommy. "It hasn't been an easy discussion to have, especially coming after our disappointment in not electing Midge. But despite my own misgivings, I know we've come to the right decision."

We shuffled out of the board room and headed up to the gatehouse. I walked arm in arm with Midge but we didn't speak until we were nearly home.

"Are we doing the right thing Dave?" Midge asked. I wasn't sure what she meant. "What, getting married?"

"I mean these redundancies you daft bugger. I'm not marrying you, I've had enough of that. Isn't living with me good enough for you?"

"Well I suppose so. I just get these romantic bourgeois notions sometimes. And I'm feeling particularly loving towards you at the moment."

She softened. "Well, ta love. It's lovely being with you, but just forget the wedding bells."

We got back and I made my speciality meal – lamb curry and rice, with samosas. We had an early night, but I'll spare you the details.

The news that we were laying off staff soon spread. We had to act fast to reassure most of the workers that their jobs were safe. Fortunately we had some good stewards in the shops that were affected and while they weren't jumping for joy they understood the position we were in. The headlines in *The Bolton Evening News* were predictable though. "Workers vote to sack themselves" ran one headline.

Next Tuesday was the CP branch meeting and I was expecting trouble.

"Comrades," said the branch chairman Eric Longstaff. "We haven't got a speaker this evening because we felt it was important to discuss the difficult situation at the Loco Works. Redundancies have been announced and some of our party comrades – directors of the co-operative – have had to make some very difficult decisions. Can I ask Comrade Horrocks to outline the situation please?"

I stood up with a page full of prepared notes. I used some of the data that George and our HR Director had provided, backed up by Gloria's arguments.

"It wasn't an easy decision, comrades. Quite the opposite. But we owe it to the workforce as a whole to make Horwich Engineering a viable business. We aren't in a socialist society. We have to fight for work and we can't price ourselves out of the market. We're up against big multi-nationals who are chasing the same work as us."

The first person to speak was Albert Ackroyd, just back from another holiday in that socialist wonderland, Czechoslovakia.

"Comrades, this is exactly the situation I warned against when this hare-brained 'workers' co-operative' scheme was first suggested. You can't have an island of socialism in a sea of capitalism. No so-called worker director should be justifying making anyone redundant. It stinks. I wish to propose a vote of censure against Comrade Horrocks for his behaviour in attacking working class jobs and livelihoods."

George Cannon, a time-served boilermaker who was one of the men threatened by redundancy, was next to speak.

"I can well understand Comrade Ackroyd's anger and bewilderment. My workmates in the Boiler Shop are the most at risk in this situation. But we have to take the advice of Comrade Lenin and look at every situation on its merits. 'A concrete analysis of a concrete situation'. We know the work isn't there. We clock in and to be honest we could be going home at 12.00 there's so little for us to do, even though we've diversified into other areas of work apart from locomotive boilers. This workers' co-operative is a brave experiment, just like UCS on Clydeside has been. If the work-in hadn't have happened, and the decision to take over the business hadn't been made, nobody would be working at Horwich Loco Works today. To mention another great Marxist, Antonio Gramsci, we are fighting what he termed a 'war of position'. Brave struggles like this, here in Horwich, help take the workers' cause forward, bit by bit. Yes, it won't usher in the socialist utopia. We've just seen people re-elect Thatcher for the second time. People aren't yearning for what we used to call 'the sunny uplands of socialism'. They want a house to live in, food on their plate, a job. What the workers are showing is that we are capable of running our own industries. We don't need consultants, public school toffs, telling us what to do. We're doing it for ourselves, with help from our friends. We should get behind the decision of the co-operative and support them. We aren't like the ultra-left mouthing slogans that are a lot of hot air. We have the responsibility to keep the Works going, and if that means I have to take redundancy, I will."

A couple more comrades stood up to speak. Jim Lee backed George's assessment and his wife Penny added her support.

George's intervention had swung it. Ackroyd couldn't even get a seconder for his motion of censure so he had the embarrassment of seeing his motion fall. We got his resignation a week later, announcing he'd joined the neo-stalinist breakaway, The New Communist Party. The meeting continued.

"Can we move on them to the next item on the agenda, *The Morning Star* Jumble sale at the Labour Club?" asked the chairman.

25

The golden age of steam

The unions put on a show of mock outrage at the job losses but agreed terms, quicker than we expected. Gloria was a canny negotiator and had a better deal up her sleeve than the one we'd tabled. To her credit, when the unions 'demanded' improved severance terms, Gloria at first played hard to get but finally gave them more than what they'd asked for. I had mixed feelings about this generosity – the money had to come from somewhere and we desperately needed capital to invest in new equipment for the Erecting Shop, as well as new IT.

The Big Hammer

"When I was in textiles David," she explained, "I saw factory owners in tears having to close mills down and make men they'd grown up with go on the dole. It isn't easy. But we owe it to these men to offer them the best possible terms. And two other things – the last thing we want is a strike, and we want to make sure that as many of the men as possible take voluntary redundancy."

"You're a clever operator Mrs Tomlinson, I've got to hand it to you."

"Years of practice young man. As you well know, never under-estimate the power of an older woman."

As it turned out, we didn't have to make anyone compulsorily redundant. We ended up re-employing some of the men we laid off, through a strange turn of events.

The call came through to George, who passed it on to the board meeting which was taking place the following day.

"Ladies and gentlemen I've had some interesting news. Yesterday I received a call from the general manager of the Irwell Valley Steam Railway. He asked if we would be able to overhaul one of their locomotives, which happens to have been built here at Horwich in the 1950s. It's in bad shape and needs a new boiler, major work on the valve gear, wheels require turning and various other jobs doing to make her roadworthy. They've mounted an appeal and have raised £180,000 to get the job done. They want to know if we have the skills to do a good job. I took a risk and said we had. So forgive my impetuosity. What do you think?"

George was a bit of steam crank on the quiet and he obviously wanted the work, regardless of whether it was a sound economic proposition or not. Gloria brought a degree of realism to the proceedings.

"Well George, you were a bit previous in taking this job on without referring it to the board first, and I've a few questions to ask. First of all, can we do the job? Do we still have the skills to re-build a steam locomotive? And secondly, is the price they're offering realistic? It sounds like a lot of work involved. Loss leaders are all very well, but often they just lead to more losses."

George had obviously given it some thought. "Yes, we can do it. We might have to re-employ some of the boilermakers we paid off but I've already put a call in to George Cannon and he more or less said he'd do it for nowt – he worked on that engine when it was first being built here. And the other thing – let's look at this strategically. These heritage railways are springing up all over the country. They can maintain steam locomotives but they don't have the skills to completely re-build them. We have. We could corner the market in heavy overhauls for steam locos. It would be a useful and profitable secondary activity to repairing modern rolling stock."

We approved George's rash decision.

A few weeks' later it turned up on a low-loader. It was a BR-built 'Standard class 4MT'. Number 76096. Built Horwich 1957. For many years she was based up in Scotland but ended up at Lower Darwen depot in Blackburn and was a regular visitor through Bolton. She was coming home. But she looked a wreck. The loco had been stored outside for several years and she was far from the gleaming beauty that punters travelling on heritage lines expected to see.

76096 in BR days at Ayr depot

A couple of our lads had already been out to see the loco and gave a sound assessment of the condition she was in. Knackered. George Cannon was one of the team that went out to take a look. "It's a complete re-build – the frames look OK and the tender will do, though it's a bit corroded. But there's a lot of work there before she'll steam."

For once, *The Bolton Evening News* gave us some positive publicity. "Steam Loco returns home to Horwich" shouted the headlines. People were queuing up at the Works gate to get a glimpse of the engine in the yard, so Gloria hit on the idea of charging 50p a head to come down and see the hulk. Typical. But nobody begrudged paying. Some old guys, long retired, came along and told us how they'd worked on her in 1956/7. We waived the 50p. One of them was in tears when he saw her. "Ah never thowt ah'd live to see the day that a steam loco returned to Horwich, even if it is a demic."

After a few weeks we took her inside and started stripping the locomotive down, removing the boiler from its frames, separating the wheels, taking down the valve gear. We got a couple of the young apprentices to be involved in their project, from start to finish. Nazeer was particularly enthusiastic. "My dad used to drive steam locos in India," she enthused. "I always loved to hear him talk about them. And now I'm working on one!"

We had some luck with our restoration of 76096. George Cannon had a good look at the boiler once it had its cladding removed and tubes taken out. "We can make a do wi' this, it doesn't need a new boiler. It needs lots o' new tubes but we'll get it good as new. Or near enough."

We got great publicity but it wasn't enough to keep nearly 1,000 workers employed. We needed to get more jobs in, basic stuff – wagon repairs, electric train refurbishment, orders for brake blocks. Gloria built up a strong sales and marketing team. Much of it was down to personal contacts across the industry and George was invaluable. "It's not what you know, it's who you know in this industry," he stressed. "But they need to know that you can do the job!"

Other work – our bread and butter - started to come in, including a large contract to refurbish a fleet of electric trains from the Southern Region. After BR had closed down Ashford, and run down Eastleigh, there was a shortage of capacity in the remaining works to do overhauls. That order was far more lucrative and important than our little steamer, but nobody queued outside the Works gate to see them when they arrived.

Slowly, 76096 started to come back together. By March 1984 it was ready to be steam tested. Nazeer was given the job of shovelling some coal into firebox and we watched the boiler pressure rise. It reached 225 lbs per square inch and obediently blew off, to an admiring crowd of Works employees. "We've done it!" shouted George, dancing up and down. The cheer that went up sounded like the Wanderers scoring a winning goal.

The last job was the icing on the cake – a complete re-paint. Again, we'd brought back some of the painters made redundant the previous year and what a lovely job they did. The livery was standard BR black, lined out in cream, grey and red. The general painting is easy enough – though you need lots of coats. Getting the lining straight is the really skilled job.

When the directors of the heritage railway came down for a first look they were amazed. "We couldn't have got the lining as straight as that," said the chairman, oblivious to the slightly more important quality of the engineering.

"Yes, and she goes like a rocket too," said George. "Come and see."

We did a few runs up and down the Works yard. We couldn't take her out on the main line, but she'd be able to go through her paces when she was back home on the Irwell Valley Railway. The low-loader arrived at 6 a.m. on a chilly April morning and a large crowd from the Works gathered to give her an emotional send-off. What we hadn't expected were the crowds lining Chorley New Road to wave to her as she proceeded, at a snail's pace, towards her home railway.

Gloria, whom I didn't have down as a steam buff, was there to see the engine depart. "Oh, doesn't she look pretty," Gloria enthused. "Reminds me of some of the old mill engines we used to have, all that brasswork and smell of hot oil. Very sexy y'know."

Gloria was taking a rather exaggerated interest in sex these days, having re-established her teenage romance with Tommy Hindley. There were rumours of wedding bells but Gloria would have none of it. "We want to grow old disgracefully, thank you very much. I'm happy living in debauchery." Were she and Midge colluding, I began to wonder.

George's optimism about the possibility of using 76096 as a 'sprat to catch a mackerel' was well-founded. After the railway enthusiast press was full of pictures of her leaving Horwich, looking as new and putting in powerful performances on the Irwell Valley, the phone hardly stopped ringing.

"Most of these enquiries lack substance," George told the board. "All of these heritage railways have yards full of old wrecks that would cost a fortune to get back into working order. But one or two sounded serious. If we can get a regular stream of work, maybe two or three locos at a time, it'll keep about 20 skilled workers in employment and provide good experience for apprentices."

The next steam loco to arrive was an ex-London and North Eastern 'B1', built in the 1940s at Doncaster. Fundamentally, most steam locos are much the same – boiler and firebox, frame, valve gear, wheels. Our lads – and a growing number of lasses – had no trouble adapting to the Yorkshire interloper. But our really big project was yet to come.

26

February 1985: Council politics

Losing to Tom Simmons didn't dim Midge's enthusiasm for local politics; she and Simmons stayed friendly enough. He always supported what we were doing at the Loco Works and promoted us as 'responsible capitalism'. Midge called it 'practical socialism'.

As if she hadn't enough to do, she'd got more involved in council politics. After getting elected onto Bolton Council she'd been happy enough being a local ward councillor while she was engrossed in the Loco Works campaign. And the Council Leadership wasn't for giving any favours to a bolshie feminist who couldn't be bought off.

On top of the pressures of the Works campaign was her own strained relationship with Jack Hutchinson, the Council Leader. He was old school Labour, ruled his Labour Group with a rod of iron and wouldn't brook any criticism. "He makes Stalin seem a model of inclusive democracy," she told me in bed one night, after a particularly difficult Group meeting. "And it's not as though he has any sort of vision. He just likes power for its own sake."

"Well stand against him then," I told her.

"I wouldn't have a chance. He's bought off any potential rivals by giving them chairs of committees, with extra allowances. He can afford to treat me like dirt because I'm not important. Horwich is seen as a backwater that can be ignored. It's hard to see anything changing."

But change did come, more quickly than anyone expected. A few weeks after our conversation, we were sat in the Works Office when David Ord, the Labour Group whip, rang. "Midge, I've some terrible news. Hutchinson has had a heart attack and it's not looking good."

Midge told me she was tempted to say "you mean he might survive?" but held it back. He was a human being when all was said and done, though occasionally you did wonder. He was dead by 2.00 that afternoon.

The funeral was planned for a couple of weeks after. 'Hutch' as everyone called him behind his back (only 'Leader' would suffice to his face) had been careful to avoid grooming anyone to replace him in case he or she might have had ideas to get shut of him before it suited Jack to depart. The so-called leadership was mostly a group of old blokes about the same age as Hutch, but without the talent for Machiavellian deals that Hutch was a past master at. They were there, in the main, because it was an easy way to make a living, if you didn't take the job – or your community – too seriously. Some of them ran their own businesses, though a few had started off in the mill or in engineering. They liked the status, they loved the trips aboard – 'study visits', where they'd get pissed, make fools of themselves and come home none the wiser for what they were supposed to be 'studying'.

There's always exceptions to the rule. Jerry Guignan, who'd helped Midge get selected in the first place, was a former miner from Mosley Common pit who'd come over from Wexford in the 1950s, was Chair of Housing and had retained his youthful radicalism. His dad had been in the IRA in the 20s and he was Republican to the core. Apart from his dad, he learnt his politics in the pit, where the union was led by communists like Mick Weaver. Jerry's hero was James Connolly, the socialist leader of the Easter Rising and probably more of an anarchist than a traditional Marxist. Jerry was a hard-working ward councillor, now in his mid-70s and ready to call it a day, though some of his colleagues in the Labour Group hoped he'd put himself forward as leader.

Jerry had other ideas. He made a point of catching up with Midge during the funeral at Heaton Cemetery.

"Midge, macushla, a quiet word if I may?"

"Oh hello Jerry, of course you can. This has all been a bit unexpected hasn't it?"

"It has it has, and let's not speak ill of the dead. We all know he was a bastard so enough said. Now. James Connolly used to say "England's difficulty is Ireland's opportunity." For our Labour Group, Mr Hutchinson's sad departure is our opportunity if we want to put a bit of dynamism – not dynamite – into this Council."

"So are you going to have a go at it then, Jerry? I'd support you."

"Well that's very kind of you Midge and you're not the first to ask. But I'm 76 this November and it's time for me to do more in the garden and see a bit of the grand-childer. I'm up for election next May and that'd be a good time to step down and get someone younger instead. So no, I'm not interested in being the new Hutch. But why don't you throw your hat into the ring?"

"But I'm not chair of any committee and the old guard wouldn't stand for a woman – and a lefty – to be leader."

"Well look at it like this. Most of them are the same age as me. They're a pretty useless shower; my da kept more intelligent sheep than that lot. It suited Hutch to have them as chairs of this that and t'other because they weren't a threat to him. They did what he, and the officers, told them to do. None of them has an ounce of leadership potential. But let me tell you this, colleen, you do have. You'd make a brilliant leader and with this new Chief Executive we've got, Jemma Heys, you could really turn this place round. Go for it, and I'll make sure you get the support in Labour Group that you'll need."

Midge arrived back from the funeral at about 5.30 and I noticed she was looking distracted.

"Dave...I've a question...."

"Should you stand for Leader? Of course you should love. Go for it! You'd be brilliant."

She did a bit of quiet lobbying around other members of the Labour Group whom she thought she could rely on. To a man – and they were all men – everyone said she should stand.

"You'll keep it quiet for now, won't you?" she asked them in turn.

The Labour Group meeting was the following Thursday and election of a new leader was the main item of business. Two other councillors had put their names forward. Harold Edmondson was Chair of Planning and one of Hutch's loyalists. He disliked Midge after she had voted against a planning application for a new supermarket in Horwich that would have devastated the town centre shops. There wasn't supposed to be a 'party whip' on planning decisions but everyone knew that an informal whip operated. When Edmondson had asked Midge to support the application, "as Hutch was in support of it," she told him to piss off. "Well could you not miss the Planning Committee this time, tell the clerk you're ill?"

"I bloody well won't," she replied. "I'm voting against it, whatever you and your mates say." With the votes of a couple of independents and three Tories, the application was rejected. The rest of the Labour team, none from Horwich, had voted in favour. Edmondson, whom we suspected as having more than a purely political interest in the scheme, was beside himself. Midge's name was mud with the Labour leadership.

So no love lost between her and Edmondson. The other candidate was a relative newcomer to the council, Sultana Ahmed, a young woman who'd fought a by-election in Bolton Central after the previous councillor had returned home to Pakistan. She was on the left, a bit of a maverick but hard-working.

Jerry had one of his 'quiet words' and tried to persuade her to stand down in the interest of having a united 'reform' candidate. She wasn't for doing it and Midge was reluctant to try to get her to change her mind.

"You should talk to her, for Christ's sake," I argued. "She's splitting the left vote and will let that tosser Edmondson in."

"Look Dave, I'm not going to try and discourage a young Asian woman from having a go. Who knows, she might win – and good luck to her if she does!"

"Your trouble in politics is that you don't have that killer instinct," I responded.

"Well maybe that's the trouble with politics then – too many killers."

The phone rang on Friday morning, just as we were leaving the house for a meeting of the Works board. It was Sultana.

"Is Midge in?" she asked.

"Yes, hang on, I'll fetch her."

The conversation went on for about 15 minutes and I was beginning to worry about being late for the board. Gloria, who was now chair, wouldn't have been best pleased. As the clock was coming up to 9.50 she put the phone down. She had a cheeky smile on her face.

"Come on, let's get goin', I'll tell you about it while we're walking."

Sultana had decided to stand down and give Midge a clear run against Edmondson. She told Midge she wasn't interested in doing any deals. If Midge won, she'd look forward to working with her and hope that the Council would look at developing some more social housing schemes in her ward.

"So I thanked her and said I'd love to have her in the leadership team if elected. Getting more social housing in deprived inner-urban wards of the borough would be a priority for me. Her background was in housing and if Jerry was thinking of standing down she'd be a perfect replacement.

"Good result then!" I volunteered. "Yes love, and all achieved by not wading in with hob-nailed boots, like you'd have done."

"What do you mean?" I asked.

"Well, Sultana is big mates with Jean Culshaw, one of the other councillors in Central Ward. Jean had a chat with her in the Socialist Club last night and persuaded Sultana to let me have a clear run. In return, I'd offer her chair of a suitable committee when the time was right. And Sultana would lobby some of her other colleagues in the inner urban wards and get them to support me instead of Edmondson."

"Game, set and match to Midge then," I replied.

The group meeting was timed to start at 7.00 in the main committee room of the Town Hall. It exuded municipal elegance, with oil paintings of past leaders and committee chairs adorning the walls. All looking very self-important, mostly doing the councillor job for the status, while the day job was running mills and engineering shops. Need I say they were all old, white men? There was one exception though. Bolton's first female councillor and a militant campaigner for women's rights – Sarah Standish. She looked out of place, even slightly embarrassed, among this company of municipal male worthies.

We queued up for our coffee and tea – biscuits had been withdrawn as an economy measure at the last meeting – and sat round the table for the closed Labour Group session. There was a full house – 34 Labour members, out of a total council composition of 60. The rest were mostly Tories, a few Liberals and a couple of Independents.

Jack Haslam, chair of the Group and a Farnworth councillor, opened the meeting.

"Good evening comrades. First of all, can I ask that we all stand in memory of our late leader, Jack Hutchinson. We will have two minutes' silence."

The room went hushed as all the Group members, most of them with grudges, great and small, against their former leader. All united in mock grief, coupled with a strong sense of relief but maybe a bit of trepidation about the future.

"Thank you. Please be seated. We have no apologies and I propose to move straight to the main business, the election of a new Leader of the Group. And I don't need to remind you that, as the majority party on the Council, whoever we elect will become the Council leader. We have received three nominations – Comrades Harold Edmondson, Midge Wrightson and Sultana Ahmed. However, Comrade Ahmed spoke to me this morning and withdrew her nomination, which I accepted. Therefore it is a straight contest between Comrades Edmondson and Wrightson. Voting will be by secret ballot. Can I ask for two tellers please?"

Doreen Aspinall and Guy Larkin agreed to do the counting and papers were passed round with the names of the two candidates shown.

The papers were collected and the tellers retreated to a separate room to do the counting. They reappeared a few minutes later and whispered to the chair.

Jack Haslam stood up and looked slightly on edge.

"Well comrades, the voting is as follows. Comrade Harold Edmondson 16 votes, Comrade Midge Wrightson 18 votes. So I declare Comrade

Wrightson duly elected Leader of the Labour Group of Bolton Council, thank you."

Clapping broke out, though it wasn't universal. Edmondson stormed out of the meeting muttering about 'loony left women's libbers' and some of the other members of the old guard couldn't bring themselves to put their hands together to offer even token congratulations.

"Comrade Wrightson," said Haslam. "Can I ask you, as our new Leader, to say a few words please?"

"Thank you Comrade Chair, I'd be delighted. First of all, thank you for your support. I feel quite overwhelmed. It is a great honour to be elected as Leader of this Labour Group – the first female Labour Leader on Bolton Council - and the responsibilities that go with it. I hope, with your support, I'll be up to the job. This town – and the borough with its smaller townships such as my own, Horwich, but also Farnworth, Westhoughton and other communities – faces huge challenges. Thatcher and the Tory government have no interest in us and they've stood by while our great industries disappear. Cotton, engineering , mining. In my own town we are fighting hard to keep our railway engineering works. As a council we must be pro-active in supporting our industries. And we need infrastructure to help them prosper – roads, but also good public transport. We need good quality housing, schools. We must do more to look after our elderly. I hope we will rally round as a Labour Group and give the council the strong political leadership which it needs, working with sensible partners in the other parties and with our much-valued officers. Thank you once again for your support. I will announce my new team of committee chairs in the next few days and in the meantime look forward to a constructive dialogue with all group members."

27

April 1985:   The Project

More contracts came to Horwich engineering. Everyone seemed to love us, the media, politicians right and left. We were able to take on more apprentices and re-employ many of the skilled lads we were about to make to make redundant. Our idea that we no longer needed old railway engineering skills like boilermaking proved wrong.

The letter arrived on April 1st and we thought at first that it was a joke. It came from the 'Lancashire and Yorkshire Railway Locomotive Society' and was addressed to George – so at least they knew who was who at this place. This is what it said:

Dear Mr Barlow,

We are a society dedicated to preserving the heritage of the Lancashire and Yorkshire Railway, of which Horwich was the engineering centre, as you know. Up until recently we have had very few funds, being dependent on member contributions. However, I am very pleased to tell you that we have come into a considerable amount of money. One of our elderly members, Eric Bottomley, died last year. His will was contested but we were surprised, and delighted, to discover that he has left the society a very considerable amount of money. It has a very clearly expressed purpose – to build a new, full-size working replica of a Lancashire and Yorkshire Railway express locomotive – based on the Aspinall designed 'Atlantic' class 1400 locos that were known colloquially as 'Highflyers'. Eric was unclear as to where he would like the replica locomotive built and at the time of his death he was unaware of the very interesting developments at Horwich. So I am writing on behalf of the society to enquire if Horwich Engineering would be interested in building the locomotive. It must be constructed to full rail-worthy standards, capable of operating on the main-line railway at the sort of speed the class once was capable of, up to 100 mph.

I am yours, faithfully,

James Holden, secretary

"Well it sounds genuine," Gloria announced after reading it. "But do they know how much is involved in building a brand new steam locomotive? And do we, for that matter?"

"Well based on what we've done with those two rebuilds recently, we can work up a sensible guesstimate I'd say," replied George. "But we need to talk to them about how much money they have to play with. My suspicion is they'll under-estimate what's involved and expect us to do it at a loss."

Lancashire and Yorkshire Railway 'Highflyer'

Gloria rang up the secretary and suggested they come over to Horwich for a preliminary chat before any commitments were made.

"Could we make it in a couple of weeks Mr Holden, so we can do a bit of number-crunching in advance of our meeting, so we know what sort of costs might be involved?"

Two weeks later a very smart Daimler pulled up outside the Works office and three well-dressed but rather elderly gents got out of the car. I'd arranged to meet them on arrival and take them up to the board room where George, Gloria and some of our 'steam men' were assembled.

Their secretary, James Holden, was first to get out of the car. "Horwich Loco Works! What a delight to set foot on this sacred soil!"

 I expected him to 'do a Pope' and kneel down to kiss the ground, but fortunately he had more sense. The car park was a popular spot for dog walkers. After him, I was introduced to Frank Staveley, chairman of the society and Grant Wilcockson, the society treasurer. They were out of a different age: impeccably dressed, tweed three-piece suits, with their treasurer sporting a stylish trilby and walking stick.

"Come this way, please," I beckoned. Their awe continued as they were led into the Works offices, with its photographic display of our earlier 'products' – which included one of the original 'Highflyers' number 1400.

Photographic display of Horwich 'products' in Board Room

I led them into the Board Room and asked what they would like to drink.

"Well it has been a long drive over from Leeds, perhaps a small glass of whisky?" suggested their secretary.

That immediately ingratiated them to Gloria, who was dressed up to the nine's, looking like something out of a Hollywood film of the 50s. I was half expecting Humphrey Bogart to come swanning in after them.

Gloria whispered under her breath to Tommy "I think we can do business with these buggers, what d'you think Tommy?" squeezing his knee under the table.

"Well I hope you can Mrs Tomlinson," said their chairman. "I hope you can. We have heard a lot about your venture and we would very much like to do business with you. But I have to advise you we are not daft romantics who don't understand the realities of business. And us old 'buggers' still possess excellent hearing."

It was probably the first time I'd seen Gloria go crimson with embarrassment. Then the whole room collapsed into laughter. The whisky was passed round.

"Right let's get down to business gentlemen, and lady," announced George. "Let me welcome you to Horwich and thank you for taking the trouble to come over to talk about your proposition. I have to say it came as a surprise, to put it mildly. Nobody has attempted to build a brand new steam locomotive. The last one built here was out-shopped in 1957 as we all know, and the last steam locomotive to be built by BR rolled out of Swindon three years later. What you are asking is very challenging. We think we have the skills to do what you want, but the costs are very high. If I was totally honest I'd say you'd be better rebuilding one of the dumped locos at Barry Scrapyard, perhaps one of the 'Crabs' that we built in the 1920s. A couple are rusting away there. We could get one of those back on the road for a fraction of the cost of building new."

"Thank you Mr Barlow. Thank you for your honesty. We realise the enormity of what we are proposing. But the instructions in our member's will are very clear and specific. The money is there for the building of a new Lancashire and Yorkshire Railway 4-4-2 'Atlantic' locomotive of the 1400 class, designed by Sir John Aspinall and built here at Horwich. The money is not to be used for anything else I'm afraid."

"Right, responded George. "Let me tell you the sort of costs we're talking about. Nigh on £2 million if we assume everything is fabricated from new. The 'Highflyer' was a non-standard design when it was built, there's very little that could be pinched from a wreck in a scrapyard. It's a lot of money."

"Well let me say that that we have sufficient funds available from our member's bequest to cover those costs," replied their treasurer, Wilcockson. "But we have a duty to ensure best value for money, naturally."

We looked round the table at our own team. I could see George trying his best to hide a smile. "Well that is reassuring," he responded. "Very reassuring. I should ask if you have asked for quotes from other engineering companies? If I was you, I'd get a couple of quotes, at least."

"We've looked around," answered their chairman, Frank Staveley. "There are a few of the bigger heritage railways who could do some of the work. But we don't want to have three or four different contractors doing parts of the job. Ideally, we'd like one single company to take on the whole job and have full responsibility for the finished product. We realise you'd have to contract some of the work out, perhaps the boiler, maybe the frame. That's up to you. But the prospect of having this project designed and brought to fruition at Horwich is, I'm sure you'd agree, such a wonderful dream come true and we'd want nothing more than to see you do it. But we want a top quality job done at a sensible price. I can assure you our technical people would look carefully at the costings you have prepared, though I have to say the figure you quoted isn't that far from what we had assumed."

It was a very business-like meeting, over in less than an hour. It was agreed that the drawing office would work on some of the original drawings which were now lodged at the National Railway Museum, if the museum would be willing. A detailed business plan would be drawn up showing cost estimates. Contracts would be exchanged when both sides were satisfied with the proposals. In the meantime, the project was to be kept secret, with nothing leaked to the press. Even the workforce would only be brought in on a 'need to know' basis.

"Good. A pleasure to do business with you," said Frank Staveley. "Now would it be possible to have a tour of the Works? It's many years since we were last here."

28

May 1985 – Some news

The local council elections took place in early May. Midge wasn't up for election but some of her close friends were. We gave her some leave from her Works duties to allow her to campaign in some of the more marginal wards. The election was on May 4th. It turned out to be a good night for Labour: the Tories were unpopular, it was the tail-end of the Miners' Strike and whatever people thought about Scargill there was massive public sympathy for the miners and their families. Lancashire still had a coalfield, just about, and we'd been supporting the strikers at nearby Bickershaw and Agecroft pits. We did what we could to help and organised lunches for miners' families in the Works canteen.

There were a couple of surprises with Labour winning in traditionally Tory wards, including Horwich South, helping to boost the Labour majority on Bolton Council to 12 seats. We'd even got Gloria out canvassing.

"I'm not political but I've a lot of time for Midge, I like what she's doing on the council. People say she's 'far left' but she understands business, that's what counts."

"Carry on like that and we'll get you in the party," said Harry Fletcher, the newly-elected councillor for Horwich North.

"Don't be silly," she responded. "I can't stand that Thatcher woman but I take everyone on their merits. Mr Simmons's a nice chap, and very polite with it. A gentleman. To me, it's always the person, not the party, that matters."

Bolton Council changed rapidly. Having Midge as council leader made a huge difference in lots of ways. The officers felt able to come up with fresh ideas, including a fund to help start new workers' co-operatives. Talented younger councillors were encouraged, instead of being put down and isolated. The new chief executive, appointed towards the end of Hutch's reign, proved open to new ideas and brought talented young officers in from around the country who worked collaboratively with the elected members.

One of the influential new breed of councillor was Sultana, who'd stood down to help Midge win the leadership. She was promoted to Chair of Housing and set about an ambitious project to regenerate the most run-down areas of the town. Some rows of terraces were pulled down, creating green spaces where kids could play. At a time when eco-housing had hardly been heard of outside trendy north London, whole streets were converted to solar heating, with the creation of car-free zones. Some of the semi-derelict mills were bought up by the Council and converted to managed workspace, encouraging small businesses to set up shop with low rents and overheads.

Life was pretty good with Midge and myself. Neither of us felt any concern when she got a routine letter from the hospital asking her to go in for a breast scan. Every woman over 50 got the same invitation. But I can remember the nagging worry at the back of my mind and I can recall the exact date, November 20th 1985.

Two days after the scan she got another letter asking her to book another appointment, 'as a matter of urgency'.

"What do you think this means?" she asked me when she'd digested the letter's contents.

"They're probably just playing safe, making sure everything's OK," I reassured her. "Come on, we'll take tomorrow morning off and go down and see them at the hospital."

We turned up at the hospital just after 10.00. Like everyone else in Bolton, I'd been born there, same as Midge.

"Born here, have kids here, die here," she said as we got off the bus.

"Don't be daft Midge, listen I'll take you for a nice curry tonight, and then an early night..."

We walked over to Oncology and was ushered in quickly to the consultant, Mr Aziz.

"Ah good morning Mrs Wrightson – Councillor Wrightson I should say, a great honour to meet you. Now, let me come straight to the point, it isn't good news, but I hope we can resolve the problem. We have found a lump in your left breast and it needs treatment, urgently in my opinion. I strongly recommend you have a mastectomy and then undergo a course of chemotherapy, which hopefully will remove any remaining cancers."

I held Midge's hand. I wasn't used to feeling her tremble.

"So what are my chances of survival then?" she asked, "Please be honest with me, I don't want any shilly-shallying."

"Yes of course Mrs Wrightson. I would say you have a 75% chance of a complete recovery, but this is not an exact science. I am going by experience. And the chemotherapy affects different people in different ways. I can't say it's a pleasant experience. But most people nowadays get through it and recover."

"Right, when do I start then?"

The operation took place the following Monday. It meant relying on her Deputy Leader, Sultana, to run the Group and Council. "Thank God I've got you kid," she told her before the monthly Labour Group. "I'm not sure I'd trust some of them, but you'll do the job fine."

"Yes, don't worry Midge but it's only temporary, and everyone will be sympathetic, you'll see. And I'll kill them if they aren't."

"Listen Dave, I'm not going to be a very attractive proposition with only one tit left. I wouldn't blame you if you wanted to call it a day."

"Don't be bloody ridiculous. I'm your bloke, I love you. You'll still be you. And I'll still be crazy about you."

The chemotherapy was at Bolton Royal, so not too far to travel. It started a few weeks after the op. I took the morning off and we got a taxi to the hospital. She'd been warned of what to expect. Feeling sick, feeling like shit, if you were one of the more unlucky ones. Hair loss. And she had lovely hair.

We tried to make an occasion of it – going off to a nice pub for lunch. But she couldn't eat, so next time we just did a bit of a drive and parked up around the lakes at Anglezarke. It was early December and there was a smattering of snow on Rivington Pike.

"We'd better do some Christmas shopping Dave," Midge said. "We've got to enjoy it – could be my last!"

"Give over Midge, don't even joke about it. I wouldn't be surprised if you saw me out."

And we had a good Christmas. The Works Committee organised a Christmas Party in the Erecting Shop. We cleared everything out apart from 'the project' – our new locomotive – and created enough space for dancing. We set up a bar along one of the benches and the local brewery supplied the ale, for free. Once again The Loco Boys performed, though by now they'd all left the Works and gone professional.

The chemotherapy started again straight after New Year. We'd developed a routine, me driving her down to the hospital, I'd hang around or go for a pint in The Brooklyn on Green Lane, and be waiting for Midge to appear. By now most of that lovely brown hair had gone.

"I've an appointment for a wig," she announced one evening. "They say it'll make me look ten years' younger, and I'm sick of going round with this bloody headscarf, like Gypsy Rosalee."

Three weeks later a parcel arrived addressed for Midge. "I know what that'll be," she said. "You sit down with your cup of tea and I'll go and try it on."

A few minutes later Midge came into the living room with the new wig, beaming. "Ta-daa! The new me..."

I involuntarily gawped. I thought it looked awful - and it was written all over my face. Long auburn hair, curled up at the end, making her look like some sort of fake 1950s film star.

"You don't like it then, do you?"

"Well, it's…I don't know. It makes you look, different. I'm sorry love."

"OK, don't worry, it's no big deal. But I'll wear it for council meetings, when I'm well enough to get down to t'town hall."

What a complete twat. I felt rotten. Couldn't I have tried to like it? Well I did. But it made her look like someone else, not Midge.

That night in bed she was still upset.

"Midge, I'm so sorry. Look, I'll get used to it. It was just a shock, it does make you look different. But it's a nice wig…"

"Thanks for trying Dave, but I know what you mean. Mutton dressed up as a lamb and all that. Your face said it all."

"Wig or no fucking wig, I still love you."

"Yes, I know you do Dave. Part of me, to be honest, thought you'd find all this cancer stuff too much and piss off somewhere. I'd have understood. Nobody wants to be with someone who's dying."

"Except you're not dying Midge. You know the doc said you'd a high chance of a complete recovery."

"Well he might have said that, but my body's telling me summat else. These headaches are getting worse, despite the painkillers. So listen. I wouldn't blame you if you did go, like I said before. You're still young, it's too much to ask you to have to go through. I'll be fine, I'm resigned to it. And it's been lovely having you. It really has."

"Come here and give me a cuddle missus. You're not going to die, and I'm not going anywhere. End of. Now let's get some sleep."

Midge was called in by Mr Aziz in early February. She'd been getting some headaches and dizziness which we put down to the chemotherapy. She'd told the hospital and they'd called her in for some scans. She had the tests the previous week and the results had come back. We were given an appointment for 10.00 am on Thursday morning.

It was bitterly cold and snow had fallen during the night, making the roads almost impassable. The buses weren't running so we chanced our luck along Chorley New Road in the car. We got there with a couple of minutes before the appointment was due, only to find the consultant was running late anyway.

The receptionist was welcoming. "You're the first people to have got through this morning! Mr Aziz is travelling in from Cheshire and he's been delayed by the weather. He knows you're coming so just bear with us Mrs Wrightson. Can I get you both a cup of tea?"

Mr Aziz came rushing through the door and paused to say hello. "So very sorry I'm late Mrs Wrightson, this bloody English weather! I'll be with you in two minutes."

He was true to his word and we were ushered in by the receptionist.

"Well Mrs Wrightson, David. Please sit down. I've brought along Dr Sarwar, a good colleague, to be with me. I'm afraid it isn't what you will want to hear."

"Well I didn't expect you to tell me we'd won a holiday in Barbados Mr Aziz. Just tell me the truth, no messing about."

"Well despite a very intensive programme of chemotherapy I have to tell you the cancer has spread. There are some lesions around the brain, which is what is causing your headaches. I am going to put you on some drugs that will help relieve the discomfort."

"So it's downhill all the way, then. How long do you think I've got?" Midge asked, with a slight wobble in her voice.

"Mrs Wrightson if you want me to be completely honest it isn't looking very good. I will put you on palliative care and you have the option of having a few days in the new hospice that has opened in Bolton. But nobody can honestly say how long you – or any of us – have got left. I could be run over by a bus tomorrow. You could spend another very happy Christmas with your husband."

We came out of the hospital without speaking, holding each other closely. It had started snowing again.

The following morning I brought Midge a cup of tea in bed; a rare treat since she'd become so busy with council and Works issues.

"Dave, I've been having a think about the Loco Works. If there's one thing I want to do before....before I go.....it's to secure the future of the Works. It may have slipped your mind but the 'peppercorn rent' agreement for the site is coming to an end in a couple of months and I'd bet any money that BR will be after a commercial income out of us."

Sure enough, at the board meeting the following week George said had already received a letter from BR saying they wanted to meet to discuss 'follow-on' arrangements at the end of the lease.

"What do you think they'll be after?" asked Gloria.

"I would think they will be hoping to get it off their hands," said George. "They're under pressure to dispose of unwanted assets and they could get a hefty capital receipt for the site. The equipment is well-nigh worthless, but the land is a different proposition. It would go for housing, even though much of the ground is badly contaminated."

The board authorised George to meet with BR to find out what their bottom line was and report back. He didn't take long.

"It's as I said. They want to sell. They are very sympathetic to what we've been doing and expressed surprise that we've survived this long. But they're under pressure from Government to sell and have to go for the best price."

"Which is?" asked Tommy.

"The site has been valued at about £800,000 taking into account contamination, poor access and demolition costs."

"And what have we got in reserves?"

"About £100,000 and that's needed for re-equipping. So the picture is pretty grim. Getting that sort of money would require a huge loan which we'd struggle to service."

"OK, well let's not get too pessimistic," Midge intervened. "The Council has substantial reserves and we might be able to help. We can't cover all the costs, but perhaps half. And if the people of Horwich want to see us continue, why don't we launch a share offer to raise the rest?"

Which was what the board agreed. Midge went to see the Council's Finance Director Joe Ward, and Jemma, her Chief Executive, to sound them out. It was agreed – subject to member approval - that the Council would invest £400,000 into the Works.

The next stage was to launch the community share offer. Ed Nuttall, from the Co-operative Trust, helped us put the offer together and it was launched at a concert in the RMI Club on January 2nd. The concert raised over £2000 and we sold £25,000 worth of shares on the night. After that it was a long slog of door knocking, letter writing, community events and national appeals. The NUR agreed to invest £50,000 and TSSA said they'd match it. We got some sizeable contributions from private individuals who were either Horwich ex-pats or people who'd been inspired by the story of what we were trying to achieve. By the end of January we'd reached our target.

Some of the assets we acquired

Negotiations with BR were painfully slow and we had to pull in more favours from friendly MPs and Lionel. By March we had agreed 'heads of terms' with the BR Property Board. We would take ownership of the entire site, all equipment remaining within the Works subject to a full audit and all the buildings. Such as they were. On top of that, any liabilities for contaminated land.

Talks went on into the spring. Finally, George got a phone call from his old pal, Gordon McLeod, Director of the BR Property Board, to come over to Manchester in a week's time to sign the papers.

The day, May 23rd 1985, was a typical wet Manchester morning. George, Tommy, Gloria, Jemma, Midge and myself gathered outside the Property

Board's offices on High Street.

"Well this is it," said Tommy, nervously stating the obvious.

We were met with handshakes and cups of tea, George handed over the cheque for the agreed price of £800,000. Gordon McLeod passed across the deeds of the site, and the documents informing us that we were now the lucky owners of equipment dating back to the 1880s.

Tommy had brought along a couple of bottles of champagne. "Bugger the cups of tea, this calls for a proper celebration!"

I glanced round to see Midge, her face strained and a tear dripping down.

"We did it, love, we did it!" I said, hugging her. "And it was down to you."

"Aye, we did," was all she said.

29

February 1986:   New alliances

Purchase of the site didn't make any obvious difference. We were secure, we had an asset. Life at the Works carried on.

'The Project', as it had come to be called, was progressing. Designs for the new locomotive had been worked up from some of the originals from the Horwich drawing office which were kept at the National Railway Museum. Our chief draughtsman, Ronnie Eccles, had persuaded the museum to let us make complete copies of the drawings which we used as the basis for new computer-aided designs, which were just coming onto the market. We held an extended board meeting to get a report on progress with the modelling.

"Say what you like," Ronnie reported to the board meeting, "but these original drawings are works of art. No fucking computer – sorry Mrs Tomlinson – can achieve that sort of artistry."

"No need to apologise Mr Eccles," Gloria intervened. "But we're not painting the Sistine bloody Chapel, are we, we're designing a new steam locomotive, so if it does the job, that's flippin' marvellous."

With the set of drawings complete, we were able to get into the next stage, of procuring the essential elements of the locomotive: boiler and firebox, frame, wheels and motion.

We decided we'd invest in equipment to fabricate the wheels, and frame, ourselves. It was a risk but if we could make this work, we knew there'd be a demand for more in the future. But the boiler was more difficult. Yes, we could do it, Joe Mullarkey, our chief boilersmith assured us, but it would be a big risk. And he'd been looking round at other suppliers.

"Like where?" Gloria interrogated. "There can't be anywhere in this country that's still making locomotive boilers, where are you suggesting, bloody China?"

A wide grin crept across Joe's face, shared with George Barlow. "Well actually Mrs Tomlinson, that's exactly where I'm suggesting. Me and George have been in contact with this place called Datong, somewhere up in the north of the country, Shanxi Province wherever that is. The factory is new, it's only been open a couple of years, and it's geared up for steam as well as diesel. So they're still building locomotives there, big buggers they are too. If we give them the exact dimensions of what we want, they could do it in a couple of months. Not cheap but it'd be a good job."

The negotiations with the Chinese weren't easy. Language barriers were only one of the problems. They couldn't get their heads round the fact that we were a worker-owned company, not owned by the state, nor a private company. The irony wasn't lost on us.

Joe and George took a week out to fly to China and visit the works, and meet Datong's own boiler experts. I joined them to open up discussions with their commercial director, Mr Liu Yongxu. Meeting face to face helped overcome some of the initial difficulties. We were lucky in having a young interpreter, Chen, who understood the technicalities of steam locomotives – her dad had been an engineer at the huge Dalian plant before being kicked out during the Cultural Revolution as a 'class traitor'.

Joe and George quickly struck up a rapport with their boilermaker oppos. It's a truism that railway folk - engineers or operators - soon strike up a rapport, whatever the language barriers. At first, Mr Liu seemed quite a

The Wheel Shop

cold fish. After about 15 minutes of pleasantries I remembered Gloria had instructed me to take over a gift. I'd grabbed a bottle of 'Famous Grouse' in the airport duty free at Manchester before getting the connecting flight – not exactly ethnic Lancashire but there wasn't much else. So I reached in my bag and pulled out the whisky. His face instantly changed and he let out a cry of delight.

Chen interpreted Mr Liu's words. "Mr Liu Yongxu says he loves the Scottish whisky and it is very hard to get in China, even today. He was given a bottle of this whisky by a senior member of the Party many years ago and he became very fond of your Scottish whisky."

Production of the whisky changed the balance of the discussion entirely and Mr Liu entered into discussion with what seemed like gusto. Interpreter Chen explained Mr Liu's proposition, helpfully translating costs from Chinese yuan to sterling. The boiler and firebox would cost in the region of £150,000, which was roughly what we'd budgeted for. I asked if that included transport to the UK – it did. Gloria would be pleased, she'd added £3000 for transport costs to the budget. The firebox would be steel instead of the traditional copper, which was in short supply. But Joe and George agreed that modern boilermaking techniques using steel would be perfectly good for the job.

That evening we were treated to a sumptuous meal in the works restaurant, waited on by several smartly-dressed attendants.

"Mr Liu Yongxu says he hopes you are enjoying your meal," said Chen to George.

"Oh yes, delicious, please compliment Mr Liu and his kitchen staff."

"Thank you. Mr Liu says that he understands it is unusual in England to eat donkey meat but it is a very special dish here in northern China."

George coloured slightly and excused himself.

I interjected that we were all delighted by the hospitality and kindness of the Datong people and looked forward to a very productive and successful relationship between our two countries.

The following day we were taken for a tour of the locomotive works, seeing both steam and electric locomotives under construction. The works had a production line of about 30 huge 'QJ' class steam locomotives, which would go into service on heavy freights. The average time taken to build one of the monsters was six weeks.

"Why did England have to be in so big a hurry to get rid of its steam locomotives?" enquired one of the engineers, through our interpreter. We didn't really have a ready answer. I muttered something about labour costs, maintenance problems and growing reluctance by the work force to put up with all the dirt and heavy manual labour. The Chinese engineers pulled faces of bemusement when Chen translated. "In China, we are not afraid of heavy manual labour," Chen responded, on behalf of our hosts.

We did some sight-seeing the following day and then took the overnight train to Beijing where we transferred to the airport. When we got back to Horwich it all seemed a bit unreal. But a few days later we received the contract documents, committing us to the agreed price, half the cost paid up front before start of work, the remainder on completion. Tough buggers, but Gloria signed it off. "We'll ask Mr Holden if we can have an advance, James and myself are getting along very nicely and I'm sure he'll be agreeable."

And so he was, the cheque arrived almost by return. I don't know what was going on between those two and didn't enquire, in case Tommy might get a bit jealous.

30

November 1986:   Midge stands down

Midge decided to resign as leader of the Labour Group at the beginning of November. She'd kept a watchful eye on Sultana who'd been covering for her as Leader during the treatment. She had a different style to Midge, which both of them recognised and accepted. Sultana could be less compromising, more in your face. She had the confidence of a young woman who'd got her hands on real power, after being patronised and ignored for years. She established a strong relationship with Jemma, the chief executive, and took on some more high-flying directors in housing, education and economic development. She'd kept in regular contact with Midge, coming over to Horwich for lunches in the RMI or, if they'd more time, going out to Rivington for pie and chips in the village tea rooms.

"Sultana, listen love," Midge confided, over lunch. "I'm not getting any better. I've tried to keep a brave face on it but there's no way I'll be coming back as Leader, I might even have to stand down from the Council, though Dave is a great help with ward issues. So I'm hoping you'll take the job on as permanent. You've proved yourself as being up to it. You've made a few enemies too among the 'old guard' but you've got the support of most of the members. The Council is a different place to what it was a year ago. So are you up for it?"

"Well yes, I am Midge. But are you sure? I thought the chemotherapy had been having some effect?"

"The only effect it's had is to make me feel like shit and lose my bleedin' hair," Midge answered. "Maybe they caught it too late, I don't know. Listen Sul, I've not even told Dave this. I've not got long left. I've had a good life, I've had two good men, in their different ways. Three lovely daughters and a lad who are my pride and joy. I think I've achieved a fair bit, through the union and the council. But I know when I'm licked. I want a few months to enjoy myself, go away and do a bit of walking with Dave while I still can. And I'm stopping the chemo."

"Bloody hell Midge. That means..."

"Yes it means I'm going to die, but we all have to go sooner or later. A cliché I know. If I carry on with this treatment it might give me another six months, but six months of misery. I'd rather have three months of having some fun, doing stuff I've wanted to do but not had time. "

"How do you think Dave will take it?"

"He'll be upset. Very upset. He likes to give the impression he's a tough nut but he's a softy at heart. He'll get over it in time. He'll find someone else, I know what he's like. But he's been considerate. I don't think he's been playing away while he's been with me, though I thought he might have been tempted to go for a younger model after he'd got used to me, especially with the cancer stuff. He's my biggest worry, though the kids are going to find it hard too."

"Well all I can say is you're a very brave woman Midge," Sultana said as she stared into her tea, which had started to go cold.

"For fuck's sake don't embarrass me by starting to cry, just give us a hug, it's me as is deein' not thee."

They left the tea rooms and spent an hour walking round the reservoir. The leaves of the trees around the lake had nearly all come down, and they formed a carpet of red and brown along the path.

Anglezarke in Autumn

"I'll announce my resignation at next Tuesday's Group meeting. Don't say owt to anyone in the meantime will you, Sul? I know I can trust you."

"Of course I won't Midge. But are you sure this is what you want to do? You can change your mind you know."

"Mind's made up love. I'll help you if there's a leadership contest – hopefully there won't be and we can avoid a bun-fight that would do nobody any good. You've been doing the job these last few months anyway, people have got used to you, members as well as officers. I don't think you'll have any serious challenge. I'll do my best to make sure you get a clear run."

I arrived home that night at about 7.00 after a day in Nottingham at an international conference of workers' co-operatives.

"Did it go alright then love? Journey back OK?" she asked.

I told her it had been good enough, some inspiring speeches from a group of Welsh miners who were taking over one of the surviving pits; the usual collection of wholefood shops, radical bookshops and the like. But good people; and lots of support for what we're doing at Horwich.

"Right well I've made you your favourite tea - steak and kidney pudding, with mash. So bloody traditional in some ways, you are. But I've summat to tell you first, so sit yourself down."

"You're not pregnant are you?" I tried to joke. But I had an idea what was coming.

"No Dave, I'm not, you'll be relieved to hear. I've decided to stop the chemo. It's not helping, if anything I'm feeling worse. I'm going to tell them tomorrow and say that I want to cope with the consequences, palliative care, painkillers, that sort of thing. I'm standing down as Leader of the Council too. So Dave, I know it's not going to be easy but I want us to have some lovely times together these next few months. But if you wanted to bugger off now and not have to live with a dying woman, I'd understand, I really would."

"You're not getting rid of me that easy," I answered. "Midge, I've seen what it's been doing to you, I do understand. I think you're bloody wonderful. So we'll manage. You never know, you might get some remission. Let's give ourselves some time together, go on holiday, make sure you have time with your kids."

"Well yes, as you come to mention it the holiday's already booked. We've got a cottage in the Welsh borders for a fortnight and we're going a week on Friday."

"Oh, right…I'd better cancel my meetings at the Works then."

"Don't worry, I've done that already."

31

December 1986:   Winter holiday in Wales

We used our rail passes to get down to Wales, changing at Shrewsbury and then getting the little one-coach train that runs through The Shropshire Hills and the Welsh Borders until it eventually gets to Swansea. We got off at Knighton where the cottage owner said she'd pick us up. It was just after 3.

"Hello – bore da! Welcome to Wales" said our cheery host, Polly, as we got off the train. "You've just stepped into Wales. The border is – there!" She pointed to the sign that said 'Croeso y Gymru'. "And this is my dog, Bob". Bob was an amiable Border Collie, wagging his tail with deranged pleasure at seeing us.

Polly drove about a mile out of town, up a near-vertical hill, to our cottage. She wasn't Welsh – and spoke with a slight southern English accent. "I live in the town, the teeming metropolis of Knighton. You can walk down to the pubs and shops from the cottage, and feel free to pop into mine for a cup of tea or a glass of wine. But it's bloody hard work walking back up."

We got part of Polly's colourful life story as her ancient Morris Minor toiled up Stonewall Hill. She was an ex-university lecturer at Oxford who'd specialised in Philosophy and Politics, but got sick of it. "Too much bloody form filling, target reaching, boring meetings. I'd had enough and they had probably had enough of me too. So got a nice redundancy package that allowed me to set up a b n b out here and buy a small cottage to rent out. Husband died five years ago. Happily single, most of the time," she informed us as we pulled up by the cottage door.

"This part of the world is lovely, but I've stopped getting too sentimental about it. It has its demons, people from outside – 'from off' – aren't always welcomed with open arms especially if you're a stroppy woman in her 60s. But I've made more good friends here than ever I had in Oxford, and the walking is to die for. Bob is my faithful companion –

aren't you?"

The cottage was just what we'd hoped for – cosy, an open fire, big settee to cuddle up on and a luxurious double bed. Outside there was a garden but we wouldn't be spending any time sitting out. Beyond the cottage fence we could look down towards Knighton and across to the South Shropshire hills.

"Offa's Dyke runs nearby – there's maps in the cupboard, no shortage of good local walks, and the train will take you a bit further afield if you want. And there's a pub – The Harp – just down the lane. They do good food and it's a nice pint."

We waved good bye to Polly and Bob as her car spluttered off back down the hill to Knighton.

The fire in the living room had been laid and was ready to light, but it felt warm enough anyway. Polly's concession to modernity was installing central heating. There were several shelves of books, with some interesting titles. *Anarchism* by George Woodcock, *My Life* by Emma Goldman and stuff by Murray Bookchin, Colin Ward and other writers from the 'libertarian' left.

"I can figure Polly's political background," I said to Midge."A bit of an anarchist in her time by the look of it. And nothing wrong with that..."

"Well, we won't be short of things to read," Midge said. "She's got a good range of novels too, which I think I'll opt for rather than the anarchist stuff. More your sort of thing really."

"I was interested in anarchism when I was a student. They get a bad press – 'mad bomb throwers' and all that. But Bookchin has some good stuff to say, especially on the environment. And Colin Ward. You should give them a try."

"Ah, trying to educate me again young David. Too late for that chuck. I thought you'd have given me up as a lost cause by now, a milk-and-water social democrat..."

"You get things done Midge, even in a few months you've made a difference on the Council as Leader. On top of everything you've done at the Works and in the union."

"Flattery will get you everywhere, kid. But I think that's in the past now. Let's not dwell on it. We're on holiday."

"So...straight to bed...or a pint in the pub?" I enquired.

"Bed? At this time of day? It's not 5 o'clock yet?" Midge feigned shock at the suggestion. "Let's see what the local's like, and then you might be in with a chance later..."

We walked down to the pub, about half way towards Knighton at the crossroads. It had kept its thatched roof and had the look of a traditional country boozer. We entered and a few locals – farming people by the look of them, turned round and nodded acknowledgment. There was an elderly woman serving at the bar, probably in her mid 70s, smartly turned out.

"Good evening, what can ah get for yo'?" There was a noticeable Lancashire twang in her accent, certainly not Welsh.

"A pint and half of bitter please."

"Righto...so where are you folk from then? On holiday? You sound like you're from my neck of the woods..."

We live near Bolton. Do you know it?"

"Know it? I was brought up in Horwich. My dad, and grandad, both served their time at the Loco Works. I hear they're trying to shut it down now. A bloody shame."

Midge was delighted at this unexpected discovery. "We live in Horwich!...and we're involved in saving the Works and running it as an independent business, by the workers. So what was the name of your dad?"

"Fred Wrigley," she replied. "He was a coppersmith, like his dad. See, there's a picture of him up there, behind the bar."

She pointed to a photo which looked like it was taken in the 30s, with a group of proud looking men in overalls standing in front of one of Horwich's 'Lanky Dreadnoughts'. "It would have broken his heart to see the Works close, so I'm fain that you're trying to save it. See, I'm slipping back into Lancashire talk!"

Midge had heard of a Wrigley in the boiler shop but he'd retired before she started. "Amazing isn't it, you try and get away from that bloody place and have a quiet holiday, but you can't!"

It turned out that Josie – her married name was Wilkinson – had moved down to Knighton in the 1960s. They'd run a pub in Bolton but fancied the rural life. The Harp came up and they decided to go for it.

"We miss Horwich, especially walking up the Pike. But it's lovely down here. You don't get any trouble apart from the young farming lads having a bit too much sometimes, but Bill can control that. It's still mostly farming round here, apart from the towel mill in Knighton, though we've heard that's closing down."

"So does it feel very different being in Wales? Do you have to speak a bit of Welsh?"

"Oh no love, they don't speak Welsh round here. It's sort of an in-between accent, an in-between place really. Not quite Welsh, not quite English. To me, it sounds more like Herefordshire, the accent. The lads will support Wales in the rugby but they don't speak the lingo. You'd have to go a few miles further on, into real Welsh Wales up in the hills, to hear anyone speaking Welsh. Mostly the old farmers. Grumpy buggers some of 'em, until you get to know them. The Welsh is dying out, like the old Lancashire dialect at home."

We sat down and enjoyed our beer, brewed in the old independent brewery at nearby Bishop's Castle.

"Well this is nice, isn't it Dave? I could spend a few weeks here, get the batteries re-charged, not have to worry about balance sheets and targets – or the you-know-what...but that follows you round."

"So are you feeling OK for now? If you're up to it we can do a bit of Offa's Dyke tomorrow and treat ourselves to lunch in Presteigne. According to the guide there's a couple of nice pubs there."

About half an hour later the door opened and Polly walked in.

"Hello, thought I might find you two here. My daughter lives up the lane and I'm baby-sitting this evening, so thought I'd brace myself with a drink before starting my duties. Are you ready for a top up?" she asked, looking at our near-empty glasses.

"Well thanks I responded, but can't we get you one? You went to the trouble of picking us up at the station."

"All part of the service, what are you having?"

We had the same again and invited Polly to join us, after she'd exchanged pleasantries with Josie and some of the old boys at the bar.

"Everything OK in the cottage then? It's isn't The Ritz but it's cosy and it's the time of year for getting a fire going. I don't get that many guests in winter, and to be honest I'm not too bothered. But it can be a lovely time, coming up to Christmas. They say we might be getting some snow in the next day or two. You could be stranded!"

At the end of the week we didn't want to leave. We became good friends with Polly, though we avoided the subject that was on both of our minds. We talked anarchism, poetry, Welsh nationalism, and our campaign to save the Works. Polly dropped us off at the station and saw us onto the little single coach train. She gave Midge a warm hug and turned to me as I got on behind her. "Look after her my lovely, and look after yourself too. I hope I'll see you both again. Be strong."

32

January 1987: Midge

Christmas was a sort of 'phoney war' in Midge's 'battle' with cancer. People talk about 'battles with cancer' as though there it's some sort of war game in which you can outwit the enemy. Be nice if you could, but the disease usually has overwhelming superiority. How often do you hear about people 'winning their battle against cancer?' Never – at least not then. It's always 'they fought a long and courageous battle against cancer' or some sort of cliché like that. But they always die. And we both knew Midge was going to die, though we tried to live a sort of lie that somehow she'd get better. We even planned summer holidays, but never quite got round to making the bookings. What we didn't know was how fast it would be.

We got through Christmas pretty well. Midge was well enough to walk up Rivington Pike on Boxing Day. But it wasn't easy. Forget all the romantic shit about people dying and being ever so nice and resigned to it. Midge, at times, was raging. Sometimes she'd get irrational dislikes of people. Gloria, for one. "Don't bring that fucking woman into this house, right?"

What had Gloria done to upset her? There wasn't rhyme nor reason to it, and it was hard explaining to Gloria that it was best if she didn't call round.

"Don't worry Dave, I know what it's like. My sister had it, and it killed her. My God she had a nasty side to her when she got ill. It wasn't rational, it wasn't her. So I do understand, and I understand what you're going through. Come round for a brew whenever you like – here, use this shoulder to cry on if you need it."

It was two days after New Year that Midge said she was feeling crap. "I need to go to bed Dave, I know it's the middle of the day but I feel terrible. Just pull the curtains to, will you?"

She hardly got out of bed for the next five days. The doctor came round and you could tell it all from his expression.

"Midge is a very sick lady, David. Can I suggest we get her into the hospice for a few days to give you a bit of a break? It can't be easy for you and Midge will get top class care."

We agreed that Midge would go into Heaton Hospice, on Chorley New Road. It was near to Horwich and on the bus route so I could pop back and forwards whenever need be. She went in to the hospice on Thursday January 12th.

The idea of a 'hospice' can give people the shivers. We're frightened of death, and anything connected with it. But most hospices are warm, comfortable places. And I've known two or three in my time. They are bright, colourful, with friendly staff. But I couldn't do their job, give me the Spring Smithy any day of the week. They see young people, other folk like Midge, still with lots to offer, facing death.

She had her own room, looking out onto a garden. "When I'm better I'll do a bit of volunteering here," she told me.

"Yes, I'll come and help. Learn a bit of gardening, be good for me."

The consultant, Dr Aziz, saw me a couple of days after Midge had settled in.

"She is an amazing woman, lots of strength there. But she's very poorly. You know you have to face the worst David."

"Yes, thanks for being up front. How long would you say she's got?"

"It's really hard to know with these things. She could hang on for two months. She is getting good treatment and isn't in very much pain. We'll make sure of that, please trust us. But it could be faster."

The drugs she was on made her delirious at times. She'd go into rants about minor points of council procedure. It was almost comical. Points of order, can we move to the vote, speak through the chair....

Three days after my chat with Dr Aziz she was clearly getting worse. Her kids had been up to see her and I promised I'd be in touch if her condition worsened. It seemed like it was time to ring them up. I spoke to Jackie and she said she'd contact the others. "Thanks Dave, we'll be up tomorrow. Look after yourself love."

It was a big relief having Midge's kids – kids? They were in their 30s – and they took turns being beside her bedside. The following night I was alone with Midge and thinking about going home. It was past 11.00.

One of the nurses came over and had a look at Midge, who was now barely conscious. "Mr Horrocks, you could stay over if you like, there's a spare bedroom for relatives you know."

I don't know why I didn't stay. Part of me was so exhausted I just wanted to get into my own bed. Maybe part of me couldn't face the reality that this was the beginning of the end and some sort of normality had to be maintained.

"No, thanks but I'll just be in time for the last bus if I go now. But please ring me, any time, if she gets any worse. Please."

"Yes of course, we've got your number. She's not in any pain, don't worry."

I got home and went straight to bed. Knackered. I'd not had much sleep for days and was worn out.

The phone rang at 2.15 in the morning. At first I couldn't work out what it was, then got sufficiently conscious to run down the stairs to pick the receiver up just as it went dead. Shit shit shit. I rang the hospice back.

"We just tried ringing you Mr Horrocks. I'm afraid Mrs Wrightson is deteriorating quite rapidly. If you can get down…"

I was out of the door and on my bike in two minutes, racing down Chorley New Road as fast as I could. I pulled up outside the hospice doors and rang the bell. It seemed hours, probably just two minutes, before a nurse appeared. Her expression said it all.

"I'm really sorry Mr Horrocks, Midge passed away just five minutes ago. Please, come in. I'll make you a cup of tea."

I sat down beside her, my dear lovely Midge. It seemed that some of the stress in her face had gone. But her hand when I felt it was cold. I lay my head on her body, but couldn't bring myself to cry. Why the fuck hadn't I stayed? What a total shit not to be with her when she breathed her last, just because I wanted to get a night's sleep.

The nurse came in with a cup of tea. "Don't blame yourself for not being here when she went David. We see it time after time. People approaching death often wait until they are alone and just – go. It's strange, there's no medical explanation. But we see it all the time."

So what should I do now? There was nothing to wait for.

"Come round in the morning, whenever you want, and collect your wife's things. Go home and try to sleep."

I went out of the building to a flurry of snow. I got on the bike and slipped slightly down the hill to the main road. Take it easy Dave, don't do yourself an injury. I headed down Chorley New Road towards Horwich only to be stopped by a police car. Fuck.

"Where are you going at this time lad? Your lights aren't on, you could get yourself killed."

"What? Oh, sorry – I'm going home from the hospice. My wife's just died."

"Jesus…look. You're in no state to be riding a bike. Stick it in the boot and get in the back seat. We'll take you home. Where to?"

The coppers dropped me and the bike off just down the street and I thanked them before they drove off. "We're sorry lad. What can we say?"

I woke up at about 8 and rang Jackie. "Jackie love, I'm really sorry to have to tell you this. Your mum died at 2.15. I was just too late to see her. But she went peacefully."

"Dave., don't say anything more. We'll be round in a few minutes."

Outside it was white. The flurries of snow had turned into a heavy downfall and it was about six inches deep.

Jackie was organised and brisk. Sarah with husband Jim, Joe and Michael tried to put a brave face on things offering hugs and handshakes.

"Right. Mum's gone," Jackie announced." She was very ill, probably in more pain than she let on. It's for the best for her that it has come sooner rather than later. She was a great woman, a lovely mum and she really loved you Dave. So no tears, not today. We're going to get out and have a walk up the Pike. Get your boots on."

So we walked up the Pike, past the Barn and out onto the moor. The snow had got deeper. Jackie decided we should have a snowball fight. "Come on, don't be a cissie."

The snowball fight was cathartic. Anyone watching us would have thought we were just a daft bunch of grown-ups acting like kids, not the children and partner of someone who'd just died. It seemed a natural thing to do.

The funeral was arranged for a Wednesday afternoon February 3rd, at Overdale Crem, not far from the hospice where Midge had died and where dad had been cremated. She'd been very specific about what she wanted. Without telling me, she'd left detailed instructions for the service and her burial. The note was short and to the point, handed to me by Jackie.

"Nothing religious. Nothing sentimental. Here's a few songs I'd like playing. No weeping Dave, I know what a soft sod you are. "

The songs were a bit of a mixture. Some were overtly political. The anthem of Women Against Pit Closures 'We are Women, We Are Strong' and the ANC battle cry 'Nkosi Sikele Africa'. But there were also a couple of things that captured the more laid back easy-going Midge from the Loco Works Typing Pool. 'Ferry Cross the Mersey' reflected her childhood in Dingle; 'Honky Tonk Woman' maybe the more raunchy Midge which I'd got to know, love and desire.

The chapel was packed, with dozens of people unable to get in. Shop stewards from the Works, her old mates from the typing pool, councillors and council officers, union official, mates from way back. Family. Tom Simmons, the Tory MP whom Midge had done her best to unseat came along, giving me a warm hug. I saw Polly, up from Knighton, at the back of the chapel.

After the service we edged out of the chapel and I spotted Simon at the edge of the crowd. "Dave, I'm so sorry, I don't know what to say. She was so lovely…"

33

March 1987: The Highflyer takes shape

'The Project' was on schedule. The frames had been laid and the cylinders and valve gear had been cast.

We received a phone call from China to say that the boiler had been given a preliminary test prior to shipping and passed 'with flying colours'. It was being loaded onto a ship at the beginning of March and would reach Liverpool around the middle of the month.

A group of us went down to the docks to see the boiler unloaded. Tommy, George, Gloria and several of the guys from the Erecting Shop, as well as some apprentices.

Tommy gazed at the boiler being craned out of the ship's hold.

"Time was when we'd be exporting locos all over the world from Vulcan Foundry, including hundreds to China," he muttered to nobody in particular.

The boiler was lowered onto the quayside and prepared for lifting onto the low-loader for its next move to Horwich, on the following day. It would stay on the quayside overnight.

"You don't think anyone might pinch it do you?" asked Harry Butterworth, one of the boilersmiths.

"Don't be bloody daft Harry, "who'd want a fuckin' locomotive boiler?" Tommy replied.

There was some painting on the boiler which we went up close to examine. Part of it was in Chinese, some in English.

"Greetings to our English brothers and sisters! Long live peace and socialism!"

"Well," said Tommy. "I'll drink to that. Where's the nearest pub?"

We celebrated international friendship and working class solidarity with a few pints of Higson's best bitter at a pub down the Dock Road before heading over to Lime Street to get a train home.

The haulage firm rang us to say the boiler had left the docks at 8.00 and was expected at the Works by 12.30. We'd told some of the local schools about the unique arrival and hundreds of kids lined up along Chorley New Road to wave the boiler into the Works. Arrival was almost perfectly timed to fit in with dinner hour.

"In years to come these children will remember today," Mrs Hodgkinson, headmistress at Holy Infants, said to Gloria.

It wasn't just the kids who turned out to wave in the boiler. Many of the old hands, long since retired, stood almost rigid to attention as it slowly moved past them and down the hill into the main Works yard.

"I've seen enough locos come out of this place but it's th'fust time I've e'er sin a new boiler gooin' in!" said Sid Daly, who'd served his time at Horwich and worked on boilers at Crewe and Eastleigh before retiring back to Lancashire.

By June something like the shape of a locomotive was starting to appear in the old Erecting Shop. The frames had been laid and were sat on the wheels – two sets of large driving wheels, a front bogie and rear pony truck – the classic British 'Atlantic' wheel arrangement. The tender was being assembled separately and took less technical expertise. It was basically a bunker on wheels, but the job was done well, helped by the team of apprentices who'd scoured the records of the National Railway Museum to find designs and also photographs of the 'Highflyers', once the pride of Horwich.

The first 'Highflyer', number 1400, had rolled out of Horwich in 1899. One of the apprentices, Gill Rogers, did some research in Bolton Library to see what the press coverage was like when the first one came out of the Works. The newspapers reported that "Mr Aspinall's new 'Atlantic' locomotive is regarded as the pinnacle of British steam locomotive design and the men of Horwich Locomotive Works are rightly proud of their efforts."

Elsewhere in the library, she came across a less pompous account in a local dialect paper called *The Trotter*. It reported on the new locos being so fast "that th' carriages can't keep up wi' th'engine." The 'Highflyers' quickly got a reputation for speed, particularly on the long, straight section between Wigan and Liverpool. One was reputed to have reached 100 mph but it was never proven.

"Well aw durnt think this one'll be doin' 100," said Joe Mullarkey, the chief boilersmith, to a visiting group of Lancashire and Yorkshire Railway Locomotive Society members. "But she'll do a good 80 that's for sure." The chaps from the society were pleased with progress and the secretary, Mr Holden, took George Barlow, who was escorting the group, to one side.

"I'll tell you something George, I'm coming up to 85 in August. Once I've seen this roll out of the paint shop I'll die a happy man. When do you think we'll see it?"

 "With a bit of luck we'll have the job finished by early September but I can't make any promises. We haven't steamed the boiler yet and everything depends on that. We'll do our best."

"Yes, we know you will George. And a month or two later won't hurt. It's the first time a main line steam locomotive has been built in Britain since 1960, and what a delight it's being done here in Horwich!"

The party adjourned to the RMI for a buffet lunch and the old chaps entertained each other with tales from the steam age while the rest of us from the board discussed the more mundane question of future orders.

Gloria was uncharacteristically pessimistic.

"We've got enough coming in to keep us going for another three months but it's not enough. There's some job we could have tendered for but we aren't geared up for state-of-the art electric traction. Before long diesels will be as obsolete as these steam engines they're yapping on about, and we'll be up shit creek."

George leant over to Gloria and touched her gently on the hand.

"Gloria, I've been having a think. When we were over in China we had some conversations with some of the commercial guys in Datong. They were interested in more than just supplying boilers for us. One of 'em – can't remember his name – told us that in 20 years' time Datong would be a world class railway engineering centre, producing diesel and electric locos for the international market, as well as China. He mentioned that they might be looking, in the future, for a base in Europe. He asked me if we'd be interested in going into partnership with them. I have to say I was a bit flummoxed at being asked this and said I'd have a think. To be honest I thought he was having a laugh but maybe there's something in it. If they invested in us that would allow us to buy new equipment that would allow us to compete with the big boys and bid for the work which we currently can't."

"Why the bloody hell didn't you tell us before George?" Gloria replied. "It's worth thinking about, even if it comes to nowt. Tommy, what do you reckon?"

Tommy Hindley looked at his pint and put it down on the table.

"I think we should talk to 'em. Invite 'em over to Horwich and show them what we've got and what we need. If they don't bite, at least we've tried. But what are we talking about? Some sort of share in the business? How would that work if we're a co-op?"

"Buggered if I know," answered Gloria. "But we know someone who can tell us don't we? That lad in the Co-op Trust in Manchester. The point is we need capital. We'd cripple ourselves if we tried borrowing. But if the Chinese are interested in coming in with us, we'd be daft to turn 'em away."

Gloria didn't waste any time. She was on the phone the following morning to Ed Nuttall at the Co-operative Trust, sounding him out on what they'd discussed.

"It's not straightforward Gloria," he said, hesitantly. "You're a co-op and there are limits on how much a single body can invest, and I suspect your Chinese friends would want some degree of control over the business. But you could look at setting up a parallel company which Horwich Engineering could part-own with the Chinese. It would be unique in the

UK but maybe that's the way things will go in the future."

"So we wouldn't have to wind-up the co-operative then?" Gloria enquired.

"No, you wouldn't. But you could end up with a situation where the joint venture outgrows the parent company, particularly if it started to capture international business. But one option would be for the co-operative to specialise, as you're already doing with your puffer train."

"Puffer train? Don't call it that when you're with these blokes, they'd go mad. It's a steam locomotive!"

"Well Gloria, sounds like you've gone native. Steam locomotive, puffer train, whatever. Maybe you've identified a niche market but it isn't going to keep 1200 people employed is it? You need to expand and grow. If I was you, I'd talk to the Chinese."

So we did. I was part of the group that went over to see our new-found friends in Datong. It was ostensibly to talk about future collaboration on steam loco projects but we asked to speak to Mr Xi on 'other forms of future collaboration'.

We were met at the airport in Beijing and taken to a smart hotel in the city's commercial quarter. As well as the engineering guys we'd met before, there were some very smartly-dressed chaps with Mr Liu, our whisky-loving commercial director. This time we'd brought him a bottle of 'Glenlivet' from the duty free, going up a notch. It went down a treat.

"So very kind of you to remember my little weakness," Mr Liu told us through his interpreter, Chen, whom we'd become good friends with on our first trip.

George opened the discussions and outlined the progress with the steam locomotive, and our satisfaction with the boiler. "We haven't steamed the boiler yet but we're hoping to do so in two weeks' time. Our boilersmiths have had a good look at the boiler and firebox and they are very pleased with the standard of workmanship."

Mr Liu expressed mock surprise that it was taking so long. "Gentlemen, and Lady Gloria. In China the locomotive would be working trains by now! Why are you taking so much time?"

"Yes Mr Liu, unfortunately we have to wait for the Government Boiler

Inspector to visit us but we're sure there won't be any problems. We hope there will be further opportunities for us to purchase your products. However, there is another matter which we wanted to discuss with you."

"Oh really? That sounds very interesting, please tell us more because we have something we wish to discuss with yourselves. Maybe, as you say, we are on the same track?"

George outlined the situation facing Horwich Engineering and the need for external investment. He explained the company's unusual structure as a co-operative and the difficulties that posed in getting additional finance. "The top and bottom of it," George said to Chen's obvious confusion, "is that we need a business partner whom we can trust and who can invest in our business to ensure long-term growth. We are regarded as too small in the UK. Some of the larger manufacturers abroad would I'm sure swallow us up like a small fish but we want to keep our identity. But we would like to see if there is interest in your company in forming some sort of partnership, or joint venture if you like, with us."

There was a few minutes' conversation, after Chen had translated, between Mr Liu and his colleagues. At times they seemed to get quite animated. But eventually Mr Liu silenced them and returned to address George.

"Mr Barlow what you are saying is of interest to us, and is similar to what we had in mind. We need a base in Europe. The UK market is difficult but it may have reached the bottom of the cycle. There will be opportunities in perhaps other parts of Europe in future years, though not yet. As you know, our company is state-owned but we have commercial freedom. However, to invest in a foreign company - in capitalist Britain! - is a major political question which will need discussing at the highest levels of the Party. I do not know what the response will be."

Gloria stepped in. "Well thank you for being frank with us Mr Liu. We think there are some obstacles on our side too but with goodwill we can resolve those. At Horwich we have a very large site which is currently under-used. We could convert part of the Works for modern production – if we have the capital to do it. We have developed a small niche in steam locomotive repair and manufacture but it will not grow into a large business. To support our employees – who are the owners – we need to look to the future. Perhaps setting up a joint venture between Horwich Engineering and yourselves would be the solution?"

"Mrs Tomlinson, you may be correct. But while here we can build a locomotive and have it running in less than half the time it takes you in England, political decisions can take much longer! But we will talk to our good friends in the Party and suggest they consider this very closely. And perhaps I could ask you to talk to your own politicians to ensure that this idea will be acceptable to your own Government led by Iron Lady Mrs Thatcher!"

"Well, we can talk to our local MP, Mr Simmons, who has recently been promoted to Minister for International Development!" said Gloria. "It's about time we asked him for some more help..."

34
Summer 1987: The Chinese delegation

The next few weeks saw a succession of phone calls, meetings and discussions among board members. Not everyone thought diluting the co-operative by being part of a joint venture with China – communist or not – was a good idea. However, the off-the-record word we got back from 'No. 10' – via our friend Mr Worthington - was that they had no problem with the proposed joint venture and it highlighted the sort of international collaboration that the Government was trying to encourage. And the local Labour MPs saw it as being about solidarity with our socialist cousins in China. Everyone was happy, in their own different ways.

But would the Chinese bite?

Several weeks later we got a fax from Mr Liu informing us that he and his colleagues wished to visit Horwich to have further discussions and look at the Works' facilities. They would arrive on September 16th, 8.15 a.m. at Manchester Airport.

Three of us – George, Gloria and myself - met the party in the arrivals lounge at Manchester. It was nice to see Mr Liu and Chen once more, and he had brought three more colleagues with him. Our MP, Tom Simmons, said he'd try to join us at Horwich.

"It is very nice to meet you all again," beamed Mr Liu. Allow me to introduce my colleagues from Datong, Mr Shuxian the Finance Director, Mr Zheng our International Business Director, and Mr Zhang Youcai who is an important government official." We had two cars waiting nearby to take them to Horwich.

We took them to a hotel just outside Horwich for some breakfast before starting the formal discussions and visit of the Works.

"Would you and your colleagues like a traditional English breakfast Mr Liu? The hotel does a very nice egg and bacon." George informed the party.

"Oh yes please," Liu responded. "I have heard many stories about 'the great English breakfast'. And I would like to try some of your Lancashire specialities, tripe and the black pudding."

After an hour we set off for the Works, arriving on a typically dull, wet day.

"We have to apologise for the Lancashire weather, Mr Liu." Said Gloria. "It always pours down when we have visitors!"

"Don't worry Mrs Tomlinson. England is famous for its rain. But we are not here for the weather, we are here to discuss serious business. Can we have a tour of the factory first of all please so we know what the facilities are, to start at the beginning!"

George and Gloria were a bit nervous about showing the party round. We'd tried our best to modernise but so much of the kit was out of the ark, some of it dating back to when the Works opened. We could see Mr Liu and his colleagues tittering when we took them into the Wagon Shop.

"I'm sorry to be laughing," he explained. "Please don't think we are rude. Mr Shengkun was saying that it is a very fine museum, but is asking where the main workshop is?"

We had to explain to the party that this was the main workshop and despite the old-fashioned conditions we had a very skilled workforce.

"Yes, of course!" Mr Liu answered. "The important thing is that you have the skilled workers and plenty of space. Plenty. And also a pro-business attitude."

After the tour, we returned to the board room for morning coffee and the beginning of our negotiations. The local MP, Tom, was waiting for us. He had a familiar-looking chap sat next to him. It was Mr Worthington.

"It's nice to see you Tom, thanks for coming," said George, who introduced him to our visitors. "And very good to see you again, Mr Worthington."

"Thank you Mr Barlow. I'm now working in International Development and I made a special request to assist with this project, given my interest in it," he gave a very slight wink, which George and Tommy noticed.

Tom Simmons added "Yes, Lionel – Mr Worthington – is very supportive of your project, as I am of course, as you know. I understand he had some contact with you when he was at the Transport Ministry? I'm glad that those contacts proved helpful."

Mr Zheng was impressed that a government minister was meeting with us. "Mr Simmons has been a staunch ally of ours since our business began," said George. "And he has the ear of Mrs Thatcher!" While Tom remained at heart a 'Tory wet' he was also well-connected and important to the Government as a dependable MP 'up North' who didn't give them any trouble. International Development was an idea job to shunt him into where he'd not get up to any mischief.

Our visitors looked at each other and nodded sagely, we weren't sure whether it was out of delight, disgust or bemusement. Mr Liu broke the silence and said "We all admire your Mrs Thatcher – the Iron Lady! Very appropriate for building locomotives!"

Gloria had been working on a possible model that would protect the co-operative whilst allowing us to develop a joint venture with Datong.

"Essentially we set up a new company as a 50-50 joint venture between Horwich Engineering and Datong Locomotive Works. Our capital is in the Works itself, the site and our admittedly out-of-date equipment. What we would like from yourselves, gentlemen, is capital to invest in new facilities that would allow our joint venture to grow in the UK and in Europe. I think that is a brief summary of our proposal."

Mr Liu responded. "We are very grateful for your proposal and we have discussed several possibilities with our comrades in the Government and Party, including our good friend Mr Zhang," to whom he respectfully nodded. "We think your proposal is a very good way forward, both for our respective businesses and for Anglo-Chinese relations. I do not think you will regret being in partnership with Datong Locomotive Works."

The discussions that followed were long and complex and often involved our Chinese colleagues going into a huddle for several minutes to argue different points.

In the end, Mr Liu announced that his team was very pleased with the prospect of business collaboration.

"We are very happy with this proposal," he told us. "Now, Mr Zhang has a special request. He would like to be taken to Blackpool Illuminations this evening as he has heard it is a very special festival of the people. Is that possible?"

We burst out laughing and it Gloria composed herself to announce, "Yes of course, we will all go to Blackpool to see the illuminations. What a lovely suggestion."

35

September 1987:   1441 Steams

The 'Highflyer' was starting to take shape. The boiler had been tested and passed with flying colours. A few days after our Chinese friends had departed, delighted with both the negotiations and their trip to Blackpool, we give the loco her first 'static' steaming. It was a resounding success, with the boiler tested well above her normal limit of 180 lbs per square inch.

"Right", George announced, "we're in business. Let's get her into the Paint Shop and we'll do a road test down the branch line to Blackrod as soon as we can."

We fixed a date of Thursday September 29th to do the trial. It was only a half mile run down the branch and we couldn't do more than 20 mph, but it was a decisive moment for the project. We invited the chaps from the Lancashire and Yorkshire Railway Locomotive Society, and the media, to come along.

Unlike the weather that had greeted our Chinese guests, it was a bright and sunny Autumn morning. Gloria decided we'd make it something special so we kept the loco inside the Paint Shop behind a sheet. Only the Works' driver, fireman and our own senior guys were allowed in.

At 10.00 a.m there was a high pitched whistle and the sound of cyclinder drain cocks blasting steam out from the front of the loco. She was moving. The sheet was stripped away and our fine new locomotive emerged into the Lancashire sunshine.

There was loud cheering and more whistling. When she stopped - once fully emerged from the Paint Shop - there was, for a few moments, silence. We were all so totally overwhelmed by what we'd achieved that we couldn't quite believe it ourselves. Then there were more cheers, group photos in front of the engine, individuals lining up to have their own personal record of the day.

After a few minutes the loco trundled slowly down the branch towards the main line, with dozens more people, from the Works and from outside, lining up along the track to take photographs.

Our friend Mr Holden, chairman of the society, went up to Gloria and kissed her full on the lips. "Mrs Tomlinson, this is the happiest day of my life, we can't begin to say how grateful we are to all of you at Horwich for what you've done."

"Now then James, don't let Tommy see you doing that, he'll get jealous...but yes, we're as happy as you are. Let's go and celebrate!"

The next stage of the process was to get the new engine cleared for running on 'the main line'. She had been built to operate on more than just slow 'heritage' lines, but have the capability of hauling special trains at up to 75 mph. Further inspections and tests were required by BR specialists and the independent railway inspectorate. This was something that hadn't happened before. We just hoped we didn't get landed with some jobsworth inspector who'd find reasons to say 'no'.

The BR locomotive inspector was due to arrive on Monday October

23rd. The perfunctory message informed us that he would arrive at 10.00 and would want to take the locomotive for a test run to Bolton and back. Arrangements had been made with the operating department to allow the loco to run on the main line up to a maximum speed of 45 mph. The driver and fireman would be provided by BR from their Newton Heath depot. Both were experienced 'steam men' being employed as volunteers on the East Lancashire Railway on their days off.

The inspector's car pulled up at the gatehouse, where George was anxiously waiting. The smartly-dressed official, a man in his early 60s, emerged. He was wearing traditional railway inspector's attire – bowler hat, white shirt and tie, dark suit and overcoat. A man with gravitas.

"Bloody hell, they've not sent you have they?" George burst out, in mock horror.

The inspector was Eric Seymour, who had trained with George at Derby before transferring to BR's specialist locomotive design department at Crewe. Although steam had finished on BR nearly twenty years ago, Eric had 'kept his hand in' by helping out on heritage railways and passing out the trickle of locomotives that to be approved for 'main line' operation.

"Good to see you George. First things first, let's have a brew. Here's your driver and fireman – Bert Westby and Malcolm Foster. You might know 'em?"

Being ex-Bolton men they knew the 'branch' from the Works down to the main line at Blackrod. Both were avid steam men who would have given their eye teeth to work on the Lanky 'Highflyer'.

They took a few minutes to look round the loco which was simmering in the Works yard.

"Well what a beauty," Bert exclaimed. I remember some of the old hand drivers when I was a young fireman talking about these, but they were all gone by the late 30s. I can't believe I'm looking at one now, let alone about to driver her."

The cab controls, based on the original design, were at first unfamiliar to the crew but they soon got the hang of the steam regulator, reversing gear, water injectors, steam and vacuum brake, whistle and the other 'standard' features.

"Well, are we reyt then?" Bert asked. He eased open the regulator gently and we moved out of the yard and on to the branch down to 'the main line'. George and Eric were on the footplate together with the driver and fireman. We had a good crowd of Works staff cheering us as we set off.

Malcolm shovelled some coal into the firebox and the safety valves soon lifted as pressure hit the '180' mark on the gauge. "Well, she steams aw reet, that's for sure."

The journey to Bolton took a matter of minutes. All along the line people were waving to us, even though it was supposed to be a 'hush hush' event. At Lostock Junction a couple of retired drivers for whom Bert used to fire were there to see her steam past.

One of the infant schools had found out about the run and dozens of children were waving from a bridge as we approached Deane Clough. We reached Bolton and went round Burnden curve to Rose Hill to turn the engine – the old steam depot turntable had long since disappeared and we didn't want to return 'tender first'. It would have been undignified.

Eric turned to his driver, Bert Westby, while we waited for a signal to allow us back towards Lostock. "What do you think of her then?"

"She runs like a bloody sewing machine, that's what ah think. Smooth, a comfortable ride. Better than most of the stuff we had to put up with in the 60s when steam were on its last legs. And she'll steam off a candle. They've done a bloody good job these lads, ah con tell thi!"

We got back to Horwich and Eric did a detailed inspection of the loco, checking that none of the bearings had run hot and there were no signs of unwanted leaks.

"She'll do for me George. I'll send you the paperwork in the next few days. Let's get a proper loaded test run organised and take six or seven coaches up to Carnforth where we can turn her. Make sure I get an invitation!"

"Don't worry about that", George answered. "We'll even buy you a bag of chips."

The 'loaded test run' took place three weeks later and 1441 performed perfectly, using the same driver and fireman who'd done the first test run. Between Preston and Lancaster speed crept up to 75 mph as they approached Bay Horse, with the footplate inspector, George Meredith, gently tapping Bert on the shoulder to 'ease off'.

"I know you'd like to see if one o'these really did reach 100, but not today!"

The successful test runs with 1441 and the ensuing national publicity was a marketing godsend for Horwich Engineering. But was it the right sort of marketing? Gloria wasn't sure. She vented her thoughts at the November board meeting.

"We've got some enquiries about building new steam locos and maybe more likely some potential orders for heavy repairs. But we're at risk of being seen as only in the heritage market. It's too niche. We need to demonstrate we can do the modern stuff – diesel and electric – as well as the steam.

George Barlow agreed. "Gloria's right, if we want a heritage operation we can do that with 100 staff, or less. If we're going to keep this going with over a thousand we must go for large orders, backed up by the investment in new machinery that this deal with China will bring us. And we should hear soon if it's going to happen."

Within a couple of weeks the contract documents arrived from China. A new company, owned jointly by Datong Locomotive Works and Horwich Engineering, was to be formed. 'The Anglo-Chinese Locomotive Company'. The eight person board would have four representatives from each of the two companies, and the chairman and vice-chairman would alternate between the two, on an annual basis. Mr Liu and his colleagues would arrive on November 20th to sign the documents. We explained it was too late to see Blackpool Illuminations, much to their disappointment.

This time their visit was slightly less rushed. They agreed to let us collect them from the airport. We had hired a private room at The Pack Horse in Bolton and we agreed to get the formalities over before lunch. The whole thing took little more than an hour. The Anglo-Chinese Locomotive Company was born and we tucked into our lunch with a sense of relief. We'd specially asked for tripe and black pudding to be on the menu and our guests were delighted. We were on our way, with the capital behind us that we needed to survive and grow. And I was appointed Director, Human Resources. 'Poacher turned gamekeeper' my dad would've said.

I brought along a new colleague. The board had agreed to appoint a deputy HR Director – Gail Bramwell - a bright young engineer from Derby, whom George had met at a conference. She looked a bit fierce, like some of the radical feminists I'd known at Lancaster. Short, dyed red hair, wore jeans if she was on the shop floor but could dress up to the nines if she was required at board meetings or special occasions like this. Above all, a highly inventive engineer who was able to handle people and knew how the business worked. And it turned out she had other useful skills to offer.

36

December 1987:   Christmas without Midge

The months since Midge had died were busy with the Works stuff going on, especially the Chinese development. Some new potential orders, a fresh intake of workers requiring training and supervision, and interviews for some middle management posts. I was working 14-hour days and becoming more and more of an ill-tempered bastard.

Looking back, my colleagues and mates gave me an easy time. There was only one occasion when I really lost it. We were in board recruitment sub-committee when I wasn't feeling too good. We were looking at applicants for some engineering vacancies. I made some disparaging comment about the quality of the applicants, along the lines of "it would help if some of these morons could learn to read and fucking well write…"

George was sat next to me. "Come on Dave, they aren't as bad as that, let's give them a chance."

"A chance? I wouldn't employ any of these tossers," slamming down my glass of water.

The room went quiet and Chris Duggan, Director of Engineering, came out with it.

"Look, we all know you've gone through a hard time. But can't we have the old Dave back?"

At that point I resisted the temptation to thump him and instead said "no you fucking well can't you patronising twat."

I stormed out. Big mistake, sure. Never lose your temper. I got on my bike and pedalled off down Chorley New Road, working off some of the pent-up anger that had been growing since January.

I was tempted to take the following day as a sickie. After all, I was HR Director so could please myself. But I went in and made myself a brew. I went down the corridor and knocked on Chris Duggan's door.

"Look Dave, I'm sorry about what happened yesterday. It wasn't fair on you, and I was out of order."

We shook hands, and he gave me a warm hug.

"Look, before you hit me Dave, why don't you take some time out? Have a week away, or just spend time at home. Come out for a curry with me and some of the guys. You're doing too much and you know it."

"Yes, I suppose you're right Chris. In fact I know you're right."

I hired a cottage in Wales, near to where we'd had our break when Midge was ill. I should have contacted Polly but I didn't want anyone's sympathy. It was about being on my own.

But after three days I'd had enough. I kept seeing places that reminded me of Midge, pubs we'd visited, walks we'd done. I actually saw Polly coming out of a shop in the village and hid to avoid her. Daft, but I couldn't face talking to her.

I rang up the owner of the cottage and said I wasn't feeling too well, so was giving up the cottage early.

She was sympathetic but made sure I was aware that she couldn't offer me a refund. I didn't want it anyway.

Getting back to Horwich did feel a bit like home even though I had more memories of Midge here than in Wales. But it was down to the fact that our time down there on the Welsh Borders was all about me and her. And she'd gone.

The plan was to spend Christmas and New Year at my brother's new place - a large semi on Ladybridge Estate. The house had a guest bedroom and

Joe said I'd be welcome to stay over the holiday. They'd plenty of room since both of the kids had grown up and moved – Carl to Crawley, down in Surrey somewhere, where he worked 'in property'. Debra was at Cambridge, a scientist. So it was just Joe and Pat left.

Pat was kind and welcoming, though we'd never particularly got on. I never made much of an effort, and part of it was a bit of inverted snobbery over her attempts to ape a middle class lifestyle, despite being born and bred in Farnworth. She'd met Joe at The Conservative Club and they got married when they were both in their early 20s.

I arrived, with a small bag of clothes and books, on Christmas Eve. Joe opened the door.

"Come in Dave, good to see you. First things first, let me show you your room."

It was nice enough, clean, sweet-smelling. A few paperbacks on a shelf, mainly Georgette Heyer. Good job I'd brought my own, I thought.

I took off my coat and went down to say hello to Pat.

"It's very nice to see you Dave, how are you getting on? These things take time, you know. A year's nothing."

"Yeah, thanks Pat. I'm fine."

Christmas Eve was spent watching TV interspersed with some desultory conversation. Joe had thoughtfully got in some bottles of real ale, knowing I wasn't a huge fan of canned lager. I turned in early, pleading, in all honesty, I was tired out.

Joe and Pat were already up and getting Christmas dinner ready when I appeared.

"Merry Christmas Dave!" Joe greeted me, followed by Pat.

"Thanks, both of you – merry Christmas to you too. And thanks so much for having me here."

Joe offered to take me round to the pub while Pat got on with the dinner, but I declined. "Thanks Joe, you go and have a pint with your mates, I'll relax and read a bit."

Christmas dinner was scheduled for 4.00. I've never really liked traditional Christmases and the dinner was the bit I disliked the most. Too early to be really hungry, piles of Brussels sprouts and turkey drowned in gravy. What I disliked least were the chipolata sausages.

Joe arrived back at about 3.30 looking the worse for wear, slumping down on the settee. "Any chance of a drink love?" he groaned.

The two of us assembled at the table just before 4.00 while Pat put the finishing touches to the dinner. It did smell good, I had to admit to myself. Maybe it wouldn't be so bad after all. I just needed to avoid losing my temper over anything.

Pat brought the turkey in and sat it, with pride of place, on the table. We pulled a few crackers and put on those paper hats which always make my head itch.

Before we could make a start, Joe insisted we have the TV on to listen to The Queen. For fuck's sake, I thought. But take it easy Dave, it's their house. And at least I wasn't expected to stand to attention.

We sat down and Joe attempted to carve the bird. After nearly slicing a finger off, Pat took over.

What happened then had an element of inevitability to it. Joe was pissed and I was on edge.

"So Dave, what do you think of the new place then?" Joe asked, slurring his words. "Nice eh? Good area. Beats Farnworth, or anywhere else in Bolton if you ask me. It's people like us living here."

"What sort of people do you mean, Joe?" I couldn't help asking.

"Well none of your Pakis that've taken over Deane Road and Halliwell. There's too bloody many of 'em."

"Listen Joe, I can go into town any night of the week and listen to a load of racist crap, I'd rather not do it over Christmas dinner."

"Oh yeah, well it's my house and I can say what I fuckin' well like, can't I Pat? I don't need some commie Paki lover telling me what I can say."

Pat ran out to the kitchen to avoid getting embroiled further, and to make sure the gravy was ready. She needn't have bothered.

"OK Joe, well you've made your point. I'll leave you to your nice house on your nice white estate and go home. Thanks for the invitation."

I collected my things from upstairs and opened the front door. Pat stood by the kitchen door, looking close to tears.

"Pat, thanks and I'm so sorry it has ended like this. Hope you enjoy your dinner, honestly."

I went home and ended up getting a takeaway from Curry Cottage that evening.

I alternated between anger and depression. Sometimes I'd burst into tears for no obvious reason, or even worse if I was watching some sentimental drama on the TV. All the books say that grieving isn't a linear process. One day you're feeling that you've somehow 'got over it' the next day, or it could be month, you feel like shit and just want to stay in bed. I got into the habit of having long lie-ins, turning up late for meetings.

It took Gail, as my deputy HR Director, to confront the issue.

"Dave, I've booked a table for lunch today in Bob's Smithy, we can go up in my car. Half twelve?"

"Sure OK Gail, that'll be nice."

"Good, we need to have a friendly chat."

And we did. No losing my temper, but plenty of time to think, with intelligent female company. I didn't know much about her personal life, other than she had a partner called Denise and lived in Chorlton. "A drag getting to work but a bit more gay-friendly than Bolton," she told me once.

We were given a good table at the moorland pub, with a fine view stretching down across Bolton. The place was almost empty apart from us and a few furtive looking couples.

"Did you have a good Christmas then, Dave?" Gail enquired, trying to break the ice slightly.

"To be honest Gail it was bloody awful. I should never have gone over to my brother's. We ended up having a big fall out and I ruined everyone's Christmas dinner, mine included."

"Oh Dave, I'm so sorry. You should have come over to ours, you'd have been really welcome."

"Well, yeah. It's families isn't it? You drift apart. Joe's a decent guy at heart. He didn't have to invite me round. And I just blew it." I explained the cause of the row.

"Well a lot of people would have reacted the same way. It's hard to confront racist comments without being either nasty or sanctimonious. But what's even worse is saying nothing."

Our soup arrived and we diverted into talk of staff retention, training programmes and new orders.

"One thing we – you – can take pride in," Gail said, as she sipped her carrot and coriander, "is that we have the most diverse, ethnically mixed workforce in the North-West, with more women than men in management positions. It didn't happen by chance and having you as HR Director has driven much of that."

"Not forgetting yourself," I added.

"Well maybe but we've worked as a team. And we need to carry on doing that. Dave, we all love you, you're a great guy but difficult to fathom at times."

37

April 2003: The big move

Both sides of the business prospered. We kept a steady order book of steam loco repairs and did a couple of 'new build' jobs as well, which everyone loved. The joint venture – AC Loco we called it – started to grow, but unevenly. Rail privatisation in the mid-90s was a disaster at first, with no trains ordered for nearly two years; we kept going doing repairs. Then it was a mad rush of new orders. Then it dried up again. So we diversified; being over-dependent on the UK trains market wasn't a good idea. We tried breaking into the European market but that wasn't easy. For all the rhetoric about 'open markets' in Europe, it was still dominated by the big French and German companies who were determined to keep the Chinese out – which meant us as well. But we did OK with major refurbishment jobs which helped finance some new equipment.

George had stood down as MD three years earlier so that he and Enid could spend more time together going to concerts and enjoying their hill walking. He continued as an 'unpaid advisor' to the board and we unanimously agreed to appoint Gail as managing director. We persuaded her to get a house in Horwich for her and her partner. We'd sold it to them through the delights of Rivington and a good train service to get into Manchester for its more bohemian attractions.

Gloria and Tommy were doing less, though Tommy insisted in 'keepin' his hond in' between taking Gloria on fancy holidays. He'd agreed to stay on as chair for the next couple of years but hand it over as soon as we could get a good replacement. We lost some good people through retirement but we gained some talented young recruits.

Me? I carried on working hard, and mostly enjoying it. I'd long since opted out of politics. I no longer had much of a personal life. I met some nice women through work – conferences, networking events and the like. But nobody special. I told myself I didn't need anyone. It was too much trouble – Midge had been my one success as far as relationships went.

Spring Smithy –and Horwich Confetti

Our biggest problem was the Works itself. It was big enough, probably too big for our current needs, but not an ideal working environment, reflecting its Victorian origins. We wanted to recruit bright young engineers, but some took one look at the Erecting Shop – freezing in winter, baking in summer – and walked away.

It was just after the Easter holidays. Gail received an email from Datong first thing Monday morning. A high-level team was coming over in two weeks' time and they would like us to organise a full board meeting to discuss 'matters of great importance to the joint venture'.

"What's all that about d'you think?" Gail asked Tommy. "It sounds serious. D'you think they're going to shut us down?"

"No, I don't think so love. We've a full order book and we've a good chance of winning these tenders for new trains for ScotRail. But summat's up that's for sure, they're not coming over for a stroll up th'Pike."

Like George, Mr Liu had retired and was replaced by a serious young chap called Li Zhanshu. We offered to meet them at Manchester Airport but were politely informed that the Chinese Consulate had arranged transport. They arrived at the Loco Works in a couple of gleaming Rollers.

"I don't think we'll win these guys over with a bottle of Scotch," whispered Tommy as they got out of their limos.

But they were all smiles and politeness; and Mr Li spoke impeccable English.

"It's a great honour to visit your factory," he said to Tommy, rather pointedly ignoring Gail.

"We are delighted to have you here," Tommy replied. "Would you like some lunch before we sit down for our meeting? Or a drink?"

"No thank you, our flight to Beijing is this evening and time is of the essence. Can we begin our meeting immediately please?"

We sat round the boardroom table – Gail and Tommy, myself, Gloria and Sheila Davison, our new Finance Director whom we'd poached from a bigger railway engineering firm in Derby, and Nazeer, our Production Director who'd started off as an apprentice on '76096', our first steam job back in '83.

It was a difficult moment – we weren't sure who was chairing the meeting – us or them – but it was obvious they were calling the shots. The silence – a few seconds but it felt a lot longer – was broken by Gail, speaking in fluent Cantonese.

"Gentlemen, can I extend the hand of friendship from Horwich Engineering. Allow me to introduce our people – Mr Hindley, chairman of the board; Ms Davison our Finance Director; Mr Horrocks our Human Resources Director; Mrs Tomlinson, vice-chair of our board; Mrs Khan our Production Director, and myself, chief executive of the company.

It wasn't just our jaws that dropped. The Chinese delegation looked astonished. Then Mr Li broke into a broad smile. Speaking in English, he said "Mrs Bramwell, your Cantonese is faultless. Where did you learn it please?"

Gail replied that she'd done part of her PhD in mechanical engineering at Beijing University, one of the first English students to spend more than a few days studying in China. She'd been put through an intensive language course and came out fluent.

"I think for the benefit of your colleagues we should conduct our discussions in English, however." He proceeded to introduce the members of his team, which included Ding Keqiang, his Commercial Director, Wang Yang, Estates Director, Wang Qishan, Deputy Managing Director, and Xi Ping, whom he described as a 'government advisor'.

"I'm sorry that we have come at such short notice but what we have to say is important, and we hope will be agreeable to you and your shareholders – of whom you have many! Our partnership, through the Anglo-Chinese Locomotive Company, has been very successful. It has been a model for other co-operation between British and Chinese industry. We think that the business can grow further. However, there is one major difficulty which holds back our joint progress."

"Oh aye, here we go," muttered Tommy under his breath.

"This factory was built in 1885 and is out of date. Let me be, as you say, blunt - and call a fish a fish. However much investment we put into the factory, we will still have buildings which are not fitted for purpose. And we want to expand production. So our proposal is that we move the plant to a new site. This can include your steam locomotive engineering

Out-dated equipment and working conditions

facility as well. Our friends in the Chinese Consulate in Manchester have assisted us with some specialist property advice and we have identified a large site quite near to Hor-witch. In addition, we have identified a possible buyer for the existing site, for a large housing project. We would like your agreement to proceed with the transition. The sale of the land, which you own of course, will help finance the purchase of the new site."

Tommy responded first. "Thank you for being so open with us. What you're suggesting needs a lot of thought. Where is the site you have identified? How will our workers get to the new plant? Will they all be re-employed?" We will need to put the idea to the workforce, who are our shareholders, as you know."

"Yes, of course Mr Hindley. We fully realise that. But let me assure you that the site is only less than two miles away and can be easily connected to the railway network. We will provide transport for all workers at ACLCo. who want to travel from Hor-wich to the new factory, and they will find that working conditions will be very much better than what they have now."

Tommy asked for a short adjournment so that our side could discuss the bombshell. We re-convened in the canteen.

"Well what do you think? It'll be more difficult for a lot of the workforce to get there – I know the place they're talking about and it's a good two miles – more like four," I chipped in.

"Yes, but we know they're right about the buildings," said Tommy. "They've had it. We're more like a museum, without any of the prettification. It's not changed much since my dad worked here in the 60s, or even his dad before the war. We need that investment, and we don't want to scare them off."

Gail added her own thoughts. "The case is overwhelming. If they'll finance a new facility it will transform our business and help us attract top calibre staff at all levels."

"She's right," agreed Gloria. "Me and Tommy have only a year or two left before we hang up our clogs for good – been meaning to tell you this but we've bought a little place on the Isle of Man. It would be a good clean break, a new factory, state-of-the-art equipment, warm, clean, good conditions. Let's face it, most of the guys drive here anyway and some of them living over Wigan way will be nearer. What do you think Nazeer?"

"To be honest, it can't happen soon enough. It isn't a good working environment for what we're doing. We're putting people off by this Victorian prison they have to work in. It gets so ....cold. Or too hot. It's never right and we need a clean modern environment to do a proper job."

We agreed to go back to the full meeting and promised the Chinese that we would put the proposal to the workforce – our shareholders – with a positive recommendation.

"So, you cannot make an immediate commitment?' asked Mr Xi.

"It won't take long," responded Tommy. "We will call a meeting of the shop stewards this afternoon and get their support, and tomorrow we will have a mass meeting of all the workforce and recommend we accept your proposal."

"So you do not have to ask for your Government's permission?' persisted Xi.

"No, but we will need to get planning permission from the local council to build the factory," said Tommy.

Carriage doors under repair and a message to Norman

"Don't worry", replied Mr Qishan. "Our consulate has already made enquiries with your local authority and they do not see any major problem. We expect to create another 500 jobs within three years, and all local authorities want that. We will get planning permission."

We shook hands and Gail practiced more of her language skills with Mr Li and his colleagues.

"Mrs Bramwell, you are the first English person we have met in the UK railway industry who can speak Chinese. You are a very precious asset to our joint company!" Mr Wang beamed, as he got into his limo heading back to the airport.

"Right then" said Tommy. We'd better get the stewards together. I'll get on to the RMI and see if the committee room's free for a meeting at 2.00.

The meeting of the stewards was easy. They welcomed the idea of a clean, well-heated plant with modern facilities. The mass meeting was over and done with in less than half an hour. There were one or two whinges about transport, from the guys who lived in Horwich. And Harry Longstaff said he'd be sad to see the historic buildings get torn down for housing. "It's our heritage, you know..."

"Bollocks to that," replied Joe Clarke from the Erecting Shop. "Heritage doesn't keep you warm; we want a decent place to work that we can pass on to our kids, not some 19th century sweat shop."

The vote, when we put it to all members of the co-operative, was nearly unanimously in favour of the move, with 987 for, 13 abstentions and two against – Herbert Bromley and Judy Chadwick, both of whom vote against anything on principle. So as good as 'nem con'.

Gail sent the email to Mr Li within five minutes of the vote, in both Chinese and English.

38

June 2003: Bonny Lasses Works Opens

The Chinese Consulate was right. Bolton Council was falling over itself to support the application, both for the new factory and for housing on the old site. They knew of several developers waiting to get their hands on such a big site, while the proposed location for the new factory wasn't ideal for residential development, being stuck between two railway lines. The area was close to Bonny Lasses Farm. Nobody knew how it had come to get the name, but it had stuck. So the new Loco Works was christened 'Bonny Lasses' Railway Workshops.' It had a nice ring.

We quickly got a buyer for the Works site and agreed terms for the new plot, which was even bigger than the old site and better located for rail access onto the main line. That would allow us to get trains in and out for repair as well as shift new rolling stock. We also got support from government grants for the relocation. The process was smoothed by the intervention of our Mr Worthington, who was now Permanent Secretary in the Department for Business, Industry and Skills. His email, sent to Tommy, was short and to the point.

"Dear Mr Hindley – Tommy – I am coming up to retirement and hope in my small way I have been able to help with your project. We're planning to move back up North – the kids have moved out and the place in Tring is much too big for us. So I may see more of you in the future, if I can be of any help. Best wishes, Len (Lionel)."

We wasted no time in co-opting Lionel onto the board. His knowledge of Cantonese (though not quite as good as our MD's) and above all the internal complexities of the British Civil Service, proved invaluable.

Construction began in the following Spring, 2004. The site was levelled and services put in. A few months later the new workshops started taking shape. They weren't as fancy as the old brickwork the Lancashire and Yorkshire Railway had used, but it went up in a fraction of the time. The last stage, fitting out the shops with brand new tackle – Chinese mostly – happened soon after.

Production transferred gradually to the new site. The last job we did at the old Works was very special. It was the restoration of number 1008 - a Lancashire and Yorkshire Railway 'Radial Tank' that was the first loco to be built at Horwich, in 1885. The loco had been cosmetically restored at the Works back in the 1960s after it was withdrawn from service. It had stood, boiler cold but polished, in York Museum ever since.

It turned out that our friends in the L&Y Locomotive Society had a bit of money left in the kitty after our 'new build' Highflyer – Gloria said we must have under-charged them – so they offered the Railway Museum the cash to bring 1008 back into working order, and specified that we had to do the job. How could we refuse? We even got a couple of lads who did the cosmetic job back in 1960 to come down and help out.

"Whatever you do, make sure you replace the chimney," said Harry Burgess, one of the lads, now approaching 90, who'd worked on it.

"Why's that?" asked Gail.

"'Cos it's med o'wood! Th'owd chimney geet broken an' it were too much trouble to re-cast one - nobody thowt it'd ever steam again. So tha'll have to mek one from new ah'm afraid."

"Well it's a good job you told us", said Gail.

It steamed out of the Works on September 12th , to a crowd of thousands. And not a dry eye amongst them.

By then, most of the original Works had been cleared, with all the useable kit transferred to the new site. We organised a final tour of the empty workshops for former employees and people from the town. The one thing that was kept were the old offices, where I'd first met Midge. They were converted into offices for small businesses.

We wanted to make the opening of 'Bonny Lasses' something special. I had had a word with Sultana, now well-established as Leader of Bolton

Council and an influential figure in Northern politics, to support us.

"You don't want me to open up Dave," she told me. "Yes of course I'll be there – but think bigger."

So it was in early May 2004 that we got the letter.

"Dear Mrs Bramwell, thank you for the invitation to H.M. Queen Elizabeth to open your new railway manufacturing facility in Bolton. I am pleased to say that Her Majesty will be delighted to officiate, on September 10th, 2011. Our office will be in touch in due course to discuss details."

We got a double surprise. Not only The Queen but also Li Keqiang, Prime Minister of the People's Republic of China, agreed to come over and cut the ribbon with our monarch. Our project was seen as paving the way for future collaboration between the UK and China.

Neither choice was universally popular. I was slagged off as a traitor to the working class and a closet monarchist. Others condemned us for chummying up with the Chinese. But we were in the real world; China was becoming a world leader and we were at the head of the game. And 95% of people in Horwich were over the moon at having the Queen round to visit. Most had never heard of the Chinese Prime Minister.

There were two other special guests – old 1008, and a brand new train built for Northern Rail. When the big day came, they emerged from the new Erecting Shop side by side, to much whistling, sounding of horns, detonators and – naturally – Chinese firecrackers.

The speech by Mr Li was widely reported in the national media.

"Dear friends. Can I begin by saying, 'ow do?' as you say in Lan-ca-shire. Today is a very special event for both our countries. This project, here in Bolton, is much more than a local project of limited interest to the outside world. It is one of the most important international projects that The People's Republic of China has been engaged in. It demonstrates the potential for co-operation between the People's Republic and the United Kingdom. We are very pleased to be able to support this very ingenious project to make this part of the UK, once again, a world leader in railway manufacture. Over the next few years we hope to develop this joint venture to become a leading European facility, providing locomotives and trains to an ever-growing market. In the UK and beyond. At a time when Britain is questioning its future role – in

Europe and the world as a whole – the People's Republic would like to re-affirm its commitment to railway manufacturing in the UK and we look forward to seeing more and more trains being built at this factory."

39

2008-10:   Developing the product

Five years after the opening, our joint venture prospered. Orders for new trains, as we'd hoped, started to come through. We struggled to mount bids for every contract and expanded our commercial bidding team up to eight staff.

Rail privatisation was by now well established, and the rules were different. We could no longer rely on 'old mates' in the BR hierarchy, nor even friendly civil servants. We had to be competitive – on quality and on price. And we had to overcome the doubts and suspicions about both our home-grown workers' co-operative and untried Chinese expertise.

We won more contracts than we lost. We had expertise in electric and diesel trains and were able to bring some more specialist traction equipment in from China. Employment fluctuated but by July 2008 we were up to 1800 employees, pretty much as many as there were in 1983 when BR tried to close us down. The only difference being those 1800 people's productivity was 10 times what their predecessors achieved. It wasn't that they were lazy sods, they were using equipment that was a hundred years old.

An issue that was starting to take centre-change was the green agenda. 'Climate change' was no longer a fringe issue only of interest to green activists. The June board meeting of AC Loco was devoted to discussing the implications; the agenda had been set by our Chinese partners, not by us.

"Ladies and gentlemen, the question of 'climate change' is not an academic nor even an ideological question," said Mr Li, taking his turn as board chair this year. "In China it is a matter of life or death for us. Pollution is killing thousands of our people each year. In the UK the problem may not appear quite so urgent but it is our view that in years to come – perhaps sooner than we all think – this issue will become the top priority for your Government."

"Agreed," said Gail, "but what do you see as the implications for our business? We already have low-emission technology in the new Works and have agreed a sustainability policy that is ahead of our rivals."

"Yes, that is very important," said Mr Li. "But we need to think very strategically and develop new technologies that place us at the forefront of the 'green' agenda. Before long diesel traction will become as obsolete as the steam locomotive. Electric will continue as the recognised alternative but not every line will be electrified. We need to develop new forms of motive power which are very low emission and do not require the high cost of electrification infrastructure."

The discussion lasted over three hours. The upshot was a decision to substantially upgrade our research and development team and bring in some expertise from China alongside some bright young men and women from the UK and other parts of Europe. We agreed to develop a joint venture with a number of universities in the North of England with particular specialisms, who would be able to access research grants to take the project forward.

It took a couple of years before anything tangible began to emerge. Gail had identified some redundant electric trains in the south of England that were going for scrap; she bought four 3-car sets as well as a couple of locos.

 "Now we've got something we can play with," she announced to a satisfied board. "We're going to try out hydrogen fuel cells, battery power and some hybrid technology. And – I think some of you might like this – we are going to explore the options for modern steam technology. Coal is a huge pollutant and if these heritage lines are going to survive they will need something that looks, sounds and smells like a classic steam loco – but uses clean technology."

"That's very interesting," said Greg Clarkson one of our new board members, a rolling stock engineer we'd recruited from one of the big companies. "But how are we going to finance the research? Even with research grants we're talking about millions."

"Yes, there's an element of risk," responded Gail. "We are not doing it because it's fun, or out of nostalgia. Our prime objective is to come up with a new generation of 'green train' for non-electrified routes that is low-cost – less than a million per vehicle. But we know there's a potential market out there in heritage railways, some of which are big business. And we've already had expressions of interest from two of the bigger ones in helping to finance a prototype."

Meanwhile, I was doing my best to hand over the reins of Human Resources Director to someone younger. We'd built up an excellent workforce that had a high proportion of local people, selected less for their gender or race than for their skill and enthusiasm. The days when Horwich Loco Works was virtually all-white and all-male had long gone.

We'd built up strong relationships with local schools, colleges and universities and were able to offer a growing number of apprenticeships each year. Some of them went on to the big international firms but we kept a good proportion, and made sure they got fast-tracked into senior jobs. That was reflected in the composition of the board – even the Chinese side was a third female. On our side women had a majority and both men and women were drawn from all parts of Bolton's communities.

"It's like the bloody United Nations coming to board meetings these days," Tommy joked – still with us in his advisory role. "And no bad thing for that," said Gail. "But it's not an exercise in social engineering, it's about getting the best people we can, whatever they are and wherever they're from."

We rolled out our first 'Green Train' in October 2011. It was a three-car passenger train, using hydrogen fuel cells. We wanted it testing in 'real' conditions and our partners in Northern and Eastern Railways agreed to run it for three months on a local branch line to test staff and customer reaction as well as its overall reliability. Before that, it had to have an intensive couple of months being run-in under main-line conditions but without earning a penny. The 'G Train' performed well, despite a couple of initial hitches.

But what was exciting lots of people was our 'green but steam' prototype. We did some collaboration with partners in Switzerland who had similar ideas. We wanted something that was a traditional design, based on a classic Lancashire and Yorkshire loco but with a few more creature comforts for the crew, including a nice warm cab for the driver. It was designed not to require a 'fireman'. What emerged looked not dissimilar to the Horwich 'first' – the 'radial tank' 1008 designed by John Aspinall in the 1880s that we'd restored in 2003.

It was a pretty thing, easily capable of running 'smokebox first' or 'bunker first', saving time and effort on 'running round' at termini. It was designed to burn a compounded fuel that was very low emission and highly efficient.

The prototype was numbered '1009' and went into service on the Irwell Valley Steam Railway. It provided a massive draw and out-performed all of their resident locos – being capable of pulling anything that was asked of her, with low running costs. The railway insisted on having a 'fireman' in the cab, though it didn't need one. Most times it was Jessica Crampton, who fell in love with the engine.

"I want to take it home with me!" she exclaimed after spending a day 'firing' to old-hand driver Bill Frost.

She got second best thing; when Bill later that year retired she was promoted to driver and 1009 became her regular engine.

40

June 2014:   A bold new venture

Our 'green but steam' loco was a hit but we knew the market was never going to be huge. If we could get orders for a dozen more over the next five years we'd be doing very well. The big prize was selling significant numbers of our 'G-Train', both in its fuel cell or battery power versions. Or, if the client wanted it, as a conventional electric train.

The way rolling stock procurement worked, in the era of rail privatisation, was that most big orders for new trains were financed through the franchising process. A franchise came up for renewal and different bidders put in their offers. Usually, the Government - as the franchising authority - suggested that proposals for new rolling stock would be sympathetically considered, subject to a detailed business plan. The big opportunity on the horizon was the franchise for the North of England. We had a good relationship with Northern and Eastern Railways (NER) and tried to interest them in becoming partners with us in their bid. NER was a subsidiary of one of the state-owned continental railways and that was where the problem lay. They had a partnership with a rolling stock manufacturing company back home and they'd get first shout for any major contracts that any of their subsidiaries won.

Approaches to other bidders drew a lukewarm response. The board meeting in July reviewed the options.

"I've talked to all the main bidders for Northern and Eastern and they're nervous about jumping into bed with us," Gail announced, to surprised looks from the Chinese members. "Sorry, I mean into 'partnership' with us. They cannot make any serious commitments, they say, until they've won the franchise but my suspicion is that would be too late."

I couldn't resist putting my oar in. "Through the chair," I politely intervened. "Why don't we mount our own bid for the franchise?"

At first, no-one spoke. Another crap idea then, I thought.

"You mean mount our own bid for Northern and Eastern?" Nazeer asked. "Isn't that a very expensive proposition?"

"Yes, it is expensive," I admitted. "A good quality bid for a rail franchise costs in the region of £10 million, that's just for the bid itself – consultants' fees mostly. And of course there is no guarantee you're going to win. But the benefits if you do succeed can be substantial. But I'd be the first to admit it needs more development. And we've only got nine months before bids close."

We discussed the idea with our Chinese colleagues who admitted that they had considered bidding for some UK rail franchises but felt they didn't have sufficient understanding of the UK market.

"I think the suggestion merits further investigation," said Mr Wang. "I wish to propose that Mr Horrocks presents a paper to a special board meeting in three weeks' time and we will decide on a course of action."

The proposal was agreed unanimously.

What had I let myself in for? I had a few mates around the industry who were experts in franchise bidding, though I thought they'd have been snapped up for the Northern and Eastern bid already. I was proved wrong. My first call was to Derek Hood, a former senior manager on the Scottish Region back with BR and a closet lefty, close to the Communist Party back in the day. He was living in Berwick and was semi-retired.

"Hello Derek – it's Dave Horrocks here from Horwich Engineering. Remember me?"

"Course I remember you Dave, how are things in that island of socialism you're trying to create in Lancashire?"

"Oh, not bad Derek though I keep saying I'm going to retire soon. But listen, something's come up and I want your advice, and maybe a bit of paid help..."

"Oh aye, go on then, I'm all ears..."

I explained the situation and potential Chinese interest in mounting a bid for Northern and Eastern.

"Do you realise how much you're talking about Dave lad? £10 million, maybe more. And the odds are stacked against new entrants in all sorts of ways."

"Yes, I know it's a difficult one but we think we could offer something that's a bit different – and would give good value for money. And we want you to lead the bid team, if I can get the idea past the board."

"Well to be honest I've been approached by three bidders for Northern and Eastern already, and I declined. I'm sick to death of the franchising nonsense to tell you the truth, with a race to the bottom by the bidders – however they try to tart it up. But that said, I've been hearing whispers that they've got someone new in the Department for Transport that's trying to change things round a bit. From over your way – guy called Worthington. He wants to inject some social and environmental criteria into franchising. About bloody time too. You don't know him do you?"

"I certainly do Derek, he's been a good ally of ours. And what you're saying fits with our ideas; putting a bid together that's about more than just delivering a low-cost railway with no thought to the people working in it, passengers, community or the environment."

"You always were an idealist, Dave. Well listen, let's meet up for a pint in a few weeks and we can talk it over, but I can't make any commitments. Margaret hasn't been too well and I'd need to discuss it with her."

"Sure Derek. But I've a board meeting in three weeks and I need to present something to them. How about, say...tomorrow, in Berwick?"

"Bloody hell, you don't want much. OK, you've a train that gets in at 11.30. I'll meet you off that and I'll treat you to some lunch."

Derek was as good as his word and we had a three-hour long session in a town centre pub.

"Why are you doing this Dave?" Derek asked. "I thought you were a socialist, don't you think the railways would be better off re-nationalised, like Labour is arguing?"

"Always to the point, Derek. But we both remember what BR was like back in the 70s, not exactly a workers' paradise. If BR had had their way, Horwich Loco Works wouldn't have survived five minutes. They treated their workers no different from any other firm, and we were always at the mercy of the Treasury. What we've done at Horwich, with the co-operative, is more my kind of socialism."

"And the Chinese? That's not your kind of socialism, surely? It's state capitalism you're teamed up with, every bit as rapacious as the private firms you're up against."

"Yes, no illusions there. They are hard business people, but I've always found them honest. I think if we mounted a joint bid with them we could make a convincing case. They need us as much as we need them, and they want to make a breakthrough into the UK rail market, more than just building a few trains."

Within three days I got an email back from Derek outlining what needed to be done to mount a successful bid. It was scary. Putting a bid team together with the right competences was an awesome task, but even more challenging was the finance. Not the bid itself – but the number-crunching required as part of the bid. The Government's Department for Transport was saying it would be a 10-year contract and we knew that no stone would be left unturned in assessing the financial projections.

I emailed Derek back with my thanks, telling him it all depended on the board meeting in two weeks. I hoped they'd go for it and agree to take Derek on as head of the bid team.

I got what I wanted, and more. Mr Li had been busy since the last meeting and had received formal encouragement from his 'superiors' –

the Party – to mount a franchise bid if the board agreed. I wanted the bid to be a 50-50 joint venture, without the Chinese having too dominant an influence. So that meant raising the finance for our side of the bid, which wouldn't be easy.

But we managed it. A phone call to Ed Nuttall at the Co-operative Trust led to another long lunch and the eventual commitment of £5m to underpin our bid, as an interest-free loan.

41

2015: Lancashire and Yorkshire Railways

Derek assembled a first class bid team, pulling in old favours among mates from BR days who had 'kept their hands in' since privatisation, even though most of them hated it. What they all wanted was to see a successful railway and they weren't too bothered whether it was public, private or worker-owned. But some of them 'got it' with the co-operative, and took out shares.

We had until March 12th 2015 to submit our bid. It ran to thousands of pages and covered everything from proposed timetables to staffing levels, ticket income, track access charges and so much more. The 'invitation to tender' seemed to stress some social aspects too. Numbers of apprentices to be taken on, diversity policies, community engagement and local procurement.

"That's new," said Derek. "And potentially in your favour. So play to your strengths."

We did. The bid that went in covered all their requirements – we were 'compliant' – and we had a good story to tell about our experience at Horwich. We committed to building a new fleet of trains – our proven 'G Train' – state of the art green technology, to be built here in the North of England. And at a very attractive price. A bulk order for 250 vehicles helped bring the price down dramatically.

"A franchise bid is like a military operation. It needs precise timing, rigid discipline, careful attention to detail and sheer hard work," Derek stressed over a pint in The RMI Club, whose offices we'd made our base for the period of the bid. "It also needs some imagination."

The franchise covered a huge geographical area. When I looked at the map I said to Derek "Don't you think it looks a bit like the old Lancashire and Yorkshire Railway?"

Derek had served his time as a traffic apprentice on the old BR 'Central Division' based around Manchester and Leeds and knew his railway history. "Aye, you're right. Why don't we call our joint venture 'Lancashire and Yorkshire Railways'?

We got our bid in to the Department for Transport in London with four hours to spare. We'd ended up with a bid team of 25 seasoned professionals, working under Derek's command but we kept the cost down to a 'mere' £8 million.

Evaluation of the bids took nearly six months. Some bidders were knocked out before a final short-list of three merged. We were one of the three, against another British private bus company and a foreign state-owned outfit who already had four other rail franchises in the UK.

We got wind that an announcement would be made round about the middle of September. A good sign that you're in with a chance was the number of times you get invited into the Department to answer specific queries from the bid evaluation team. I'd led on the HR aspect of the bid. We demonstrated commitment to addressing diversity and inclusion, a shorter working week, worker involvement and lots more. All with clear, measurable targets.

I was asked into the Department one morning and bumped into Lionel Worthington while I was waiting at reception.

"David, it's very nice to see you," he said, giving me a warm handshake. "I think I know why you're here. Can't say anything else, but great to see you, cheerio for now," leaving me with one of his trademark winks.

We received the invitation to come down to the Department on September 17th. We arrived at Marsham Street mob-handed and brought along Gloria and Tommy as a treat, even though Tommy slightly disapproved of all this 'franchise bidding palaver', as he called it.

We were ushered into a room adjoining the Secretary of State's office and were welcomed by Lionel.

"Ladies and gentlemen, so very good to see you all. The Secretary of State will be with you in a few moments. Can I get you a tea or a coffee?"

We declined. We were all on edge, even Mr Li and Mr Wang who had flown over from Beijing the previous day, were looking nervous.

A few minutes later we were invited into a large office with the Secretary of State for Transport, Henry Riccarton, greeting us.

Please sit down, if you can all find a seat. We didn't expect quite so many of you..." Lionel said.

"The evaluation of the three bids has been time-consuming and challenging," Riccarton began. "All three submissions had much to commend them. Unlike in days gone by we have not been constrained by the lowest bid in purely financial terms. We wanted to get best possible value for money, bearing in mind the impact of this franchise on the wider economy of the North of England, its communities and environment. So I am very pleased indeed to inform you that the bid from Lancashire and Yorkshire Railways has been successful. Congratulations!"

The first cheer – more of a 'whoop!' came from Tommy and Gloria, followed by the Chinese and all the rest of us. Gloria offered the Secretary of State a kiss on the cheek, leaving a bright red lipstick mark. There were hand-shakes all round and special shakes and hugs to Derek who had led the winning team.

The Department for Transport had prepared a press release which was issued at 12.00 the same day:

"Lancashire and Yorkshire Railways, a joint venture between Horwich Engineering and Chinese Railways has today (17 March 2015) been announced as the successful bidder to operate the Northern and Eastern rail franchise and is set to provide passengers with new trains, more seats, simplified fares and more frequent services across the North of England.

Transport Secretary Henry Riccarton said: "This award is positive news for passengers, with more services, more direct connections and ambitious plans for a cleaner, greener railway, and also represents a decisive shift towards a new model for rail, with a high level of employee and passenger involvement."

Lancashire and Yorkshire Railways will oversee the introduction of new environmentally-friendly trains, entirely replacing the mainly diesel fleet and *reducing CO_2 emissions by 65%. It will also invest £150 million in a major refurbishment of the current fleet, providing more comfortable seats and additional luggage space.*

The new operator will also strive for ambitious green targets by investing in stations and depots to reduce the environmental impact of the franchise. This includes introducing new solar panels and energy efficient air conditioning, alongside a commitment to achieving an 80% reduction in non-recyclable waste from products sold or supplied on-board trains.

Lancashire and Yorkshire Railways will also oversee the introduction of:

- *£32 million of investment into developing and delivering infrastructure capacity and capability improvements*
- *30 new secure cycle storage facilities; improved bus facilities; 900 new car parking spaces, and 100 new Electric Vehicle charging points*
- *Improved bus links at hub stations*
- *new ticket machines at stations, removal of the administration fee and enabling on-the-day changes to both advance tickets and seat reservations*
- *Greater community engagement and support for community rail partnership initiatives*
- *new initiatives to increase diversity, inclusion and skills retention in the rail industry*
- *new initiatives to give both employees and passengers a direct stake in the company*
- *40% of all procurement to be local to the franchise area*
- *Re-opening of a number of routes and stations closed in the 1960s"*

We caught the last train back to Manchester that evening after a meal at one of London's finest Chinese restaurants, recommended by our Datong partners. And Tommy knew of a pub nearby that served up Thwaites' bitter. So honour was satisfied for both sides.

42

December 2015:   Simon and hidden memories

Mobilising for the start of the new franchise, on December 8th 2015, was a mammoth job. But we had the goodwill of the existing management and staff, and strong community support. The huge order for new trains meant that the future of Horwich Engineering, and a myriad of suppliers, was secure for years ahead.

It was time for me to call it a day. I now had a life that I wanted to live. It probably won't surprise you that Simon and myself got together.

It surprised me.

He'd retired from his job as a college lecturer and was able to come down to Horwich to do a bit of walking round Rivington, and when I could I drove up to the Forest of Bowland and Ribble Valley with him. I don't think I 'fell in love' with him, like I had with Midge. It was more the growing sense of companionship that drew us together.

It took me some time to accept the sexual side of our relationship. I loved being with him. I relished our walks, our trips abroad – now I'd retired from the board I could visit lots of places I'd always wanted to go. The Works had always got in the way of spending too much time away.

The 'thing' that got in the way went back a long time. Call it child abuse, rape even, I don't know. Not 'rape' but maybe coercion. Back in my early teens. I'd got to know this older guy – Gerry - who seemed a nice bloke. It was through the camera club. He had some really smart equipment – expensive Rolleiflex cameras, state-of-the-art enlargers. He encouraged me, developed my interest. He was intelligent, well-read.

It was when I was with him in the dark room one day when I felt his hand on me. I was a bit shocked, slightly frightened. But part of me quite liked it, relished the attention. I didn't let him go beyond touching me. But it didn't stop me from going back. The next time he touched me, got his hand inside my jeans. It went from that. Quite serious stuff; really serious I suppose. No, I wasn't forced, even if I was reluctant. I enjoyed the secrecy, the 'thrill of the forbidden'. He showed me 'dirty books' of men and women having sex. It turned me on. So it went further and further. In return I got 'favours' – use of his cameras, being taken on trips. The fact that I enjoyed it made the guilt stronger. What I was doing was against the law. He kept telling me, as he fucked me, this is really very wrong, as though it absolved him from blame, and made me jointly responsible, colluding with him. Could I be sent to prison?

I was 13 at the time.

It wasn't really me, I told myself. But my conscience told me it was. Try wrestling with all that. Guilt, pleasure, gratification, shame. I stopped seeing him when I was about 14. I still have the Rolleiflex camera he gave me. Bloody good camera.

So all that kicked in when things started to get more physical with Simon. Totally different, I told myself. This was a mature relationship, between two grown men. Nobody was manipulating anyone. And I still liked women. Getting involved in a gay relationship raised all sorts of issues. I'd come to find women's bodies so...congenial. More than just physical. I liked the way their minds work, the way they thought.

It took me a lot of time to find Simon sexually attractive, much as I loved him as a person. The prickliness of his skin. Just like Gerry's. I found it difficult to tell him about what happened.

"Shit, Dave, why didn't you tell me earlier? A lot of boys went through the same stuff, believe me. I didn't, I suppose I was lucky. I just ended up liking boys of my own age, then men. Why didn't you go to the police?"

I tried to explain that I felt as guilty – perhaps more – than the guy who had me. Going to the police would have opened up a huge can of worms, horrifying my mum and dad, with totally unknown and potentially disastrous consequences for me. So just put it down to experience. I've got the camera, I had some nice trips out and I had some great sex, I have to admit. What's wrong with that? But I knew there was quite a lot more to it and it had left something in my head that I could never really understand. Relationships, confidence...who I am.

So women were always a challenge. Should I have told them about what happened? I tried it once and it didn't go down well. So, unbelievably now, I never said anything to Midge. Wish I had. I'm still none the wiser in really understanding women. The big attraction of Midge was how her mind worked, her working class common touch; though I liked the feel of her as well. So much comes back to class.

Living with Simon. Who'd have thought.... It happened quite suddenly. He often used to stay over if he had meetings in Manchester. It was just after 'the great leap forward', over ten years ago. It was after I'd been promoted to Director of Human Resources. I'd moved out of the house on George Street – too many memories maybe – and got a place on Victoria Road. I was reliving the early days of the Loco Works when foremen and managers were offered homes, probably at favourable rates, in those elegant late-Victorian villas.

He was staying over one night and we watched a film on the telly – one of the old Russian classics by Eisenstein, 'Potemkin' I think – Simon's sort of film, and I suppose mine as well. We just touched fingers, then hands. And we kissed. Nothing else.

"This is a big house Simon, why don't you stay?"

"OK, you've talked me into it."

And that was it, he gave up the flat in Lancaster and moved in. He has his own room, sometimes we sleep together, sometimes not. He's a kind, loving guy, even if his politics are bonkers. Or maybe that's just me.

43

March 2022:   In a new world

It's over two years since the general election, called by Prime Minister Boris Johnson to 'Get Brexit Done'. He won a big victory and Labour was wiped out. I can imagine Midge turning in her grave at the scale of the defeat. So many Northern constituencies went 'blue', with some good Labour MPs losing their seats. One of them, Mike Rigby, represented one of the Bolton seats and served his time as an apprentice at Horwich in the 1970s. He'd stood with me on the picket line during the '79 strike. Tom Simmons' successor consolidated his majority in Westhoughton Central.

Over the years, I'd become good friends with Tom and we recruited him onto the board after he decided to stand down as MP. After keeping it quiet all those years, he told me he was gay. That would have cost him his seat back in the 80s, maybe letting Midge in. Glad he kept his mouth shut.

Brexit scared us. We were very aware of the risks posed to our business by leaving the EU in 2020. Have you any idea how many different components are needed to build a working locomotive? Hundreds, many of them sourced from the EU. You can't change those relationships overnight.

But we had one major advantage over other UK-based engineering firms: our link with China. We could still access most of what we needed from our parent company at Datong. Which was fine as far as it went, but we'd built up a strong market for our trains in EU countries. The chaos which followed our hasty departure from the EU last year didn't help us one bit and we lost a couple of big orders from The Netherlands and Italy which we should have won. But you never really know the entire reason. What was clear was that our costs had gone up and we were starting to lose our competitive edge in Europe.

But we took the Government's hype at face value and started promoting our business to non-EU countries. We strengthened our sales and marketing team. We built up relationships across the world. It took time and we're not there yet.

We won an order for our 'Green Train' from Norway and another one from Turkey in December 2021.

After winning the 2019 election the Tories had committed to investing in the North, including new railways. New railways need new trains and we won a major order for a fleet of 'hybrid' electric and fuel-cell powered trains, earlier this year. And 'Lancashire and Yorkshire Railways' continued to grow, slowly at first but now more rapidly. We had enough space at 'Bonny Lasses' to build a maintenance depot and employ and extra 200 staff.

I'm politically homeless, still with a leaning to my teenage leftism despite the MBE I got last year 'for services to industry'. Simon is my political conscience, which is a laugh. It was good of him to come down to Buckingham Palace with me for the ceremony, though he kept quiet about it to some of his comrades.

He hangs on to his faith in Trotskyism and the SWP like a deluded priest, a bit like the old Stalinists in what's left of the Communist Party.

OK. You don't want to hear my whinges about politics. Looking back, my one 'political' achievement was helping to save the Loco Works – along with Midge, Tommy, Gloria and many others. It could so easily have gone.

We saved it because we didn't listen to conventional political wisdom, whether Labour or further left. We made alliances, worked with our political opponents as well as allies, with the churches, communities, businesses. We got slagged off for doing it, but we were proved right. I'd had enough of always being on the losing side. For once, we won. And yes, we made compromises.

I never looked for a career. I became an accidental 'workers' capitalist'. I never quite believed it when I got that business card with 'Director' on it. It seemed like the culmination of a lifetime of elaborate deception, from the moment I started at Lancaster, maybe even grammar school.

Working class lad made good? A lot of the lads I was at primary school with didn't. I was a lucky exception. Some spent their lives in shit jobs. Some ended up on the bottle. A few are dead already, heart attack, mostly. Just like dad.

I finally retired from the board of Horwich Engineering at the end of last year. I do a bit of voluntary work for Horwich Heritage and help out with the food bank, which we sponsor.

Food banks? The world we're in.

The point is, still, to change it.

SONG FOR HORWICH.

Who said Horwich Works was a thing of the past,
Who said the yard had to die,
Who said the workers must go down the road,
Who'll give the reason why.

Not I said the Pattern Maker,
Not I said the Metal Worker,
Not I said the Fitter, said the Trimmer said the Boiler Maker.

Who said the workers must go down the road,
Who'll give the reason why,
Who'll Keep the town when the yard closes down,
Who'll Keep the cogs and wheels going round,
Who'll Keep the Bailiff and the Wolf from the door,
Who'll Keep their pride when the works are no more.

Not I said the Pattern Maker,
Not I said the Metal Worker,
Not I said the Fitter, said the Trimmer said the Boiler Maker,

Who'll Keep the Bailiff and the Wolf from the door,
Who'll Keep their pride when the works are no more.

Who'll tell the ghosts of the old Lanc's and York's and all of
the engines who've past through the works,
Who'll tell the shades of the old L.M.S. that closure today is
the price of success.

Not I said the Pattern Maker,
Not I said the Metal Worker,
Not I said the Fitter, said the Trimmer said the Boiler Maker,

Who'll tell the shades of the old L.M.S. that closure today is
the price of success.

How many Railway's in how many Lands are dying for want of a
craftsman's hand,
Who'll tell those people their hopes are in vain, and Who'll
tell them now is the age of the train.

Not I said the Pattern Maker,
Not I said the Metal Worker,
Not I said the Fitter, said the Trimmer said the Boiler Maker,

Who'll tell those people their hopes are in vain and Who'll tell
them now is the age of the train.

Other books by the author

The Settle-Carlisle Railway (2019) published by Crowood and available £24. It's a general history of the railway, bringing it up to date. It includes a chapter on the author's time as a goods guard on the line, when he was based at Blackburn in the 1970s. The book includes a guide to the line, from Leeds to Carlisle. Some previously-unused sources helped to give the book a stronger 'social' dimension, including the columns of the LMS staff magazine in the 1920s. ISBN 978-1-78500-637-1

The following are all available from Lancashire Loominary at 109 Harpers Lane, Bolton BL1 6HU. Cheques should be made out to 'Paul Salveson'

'Lancashire's Romantic Radical – the life and writings of Allen Clarke/Teddy Ashton' (2009). The story of Lancashire's errant genius – cyclist, philosopher, unsuccessful politician, amazingly popular dialect writer. **£15 with free postage**. This book outlines the life and writings of one of Lancashire's most prolific – and interesting – writers. Allen Clarke (1863-1935) was the son of mill workers and began work in the mill himself at the age of 11. He became a much-loved writer and an early pioneer of the socialist movement. He wrote in Lancashire dialect as 'Teddy Ashton;' and his sketches sold by the thousand. He was a keen cyclist and rambler; his books on the Lancashire countryside – 'Windmill Land' and 'Moorlands and Memories' are wonderful mixtures of history, landscape and philosophy.

'With Walt Whitman in Bolton – Lancashire's Links to Walt Whitman' (new edition, 2019) This charts the remarkable story of Bolton's long-lasting links to America's great poet. **Price £10.00 including post and packing**. Bolton's links with the great American poet Walt Whitman make up one of the most fascinating footnotes in literary history. From the 1880s a small group of Boltonians began a correspondence with Whitman and two (John Johnston and J W Wallace) visited the poet in America. Each year on Whitman's birthday (May 31) the Bolton group threw a party to celebrate his memory, with poems, lectures and passing round a loving cup of spiced claret. Each wore a sprig of lilac in Whitman's memory. The group were close to the founders of the ILP – Keir Hardie, Bruce and Katharine Bruce Glasier and Robert Blatchford. The links with Whitman lovers in the USA continue to this day.

'Northern Rail Heritage'. A short introduction to the social history of the North's railways. ***Price £6.00 including postage***. The North ushered in the railway age with the Stockton and Darlington in 1825 followed by the Liverpool and Manchester in 1830. But too often the story of the people who worked on the railways has been ignored. This booklet outlines the social history of railways in the North. It includes the growth of railways in the 19th century, railways in the two world wars, the general strike and the impact of Beeching.

Other publications, published by Lawrence and Wishart:

Railpolitik: Bringing railways back to communities (2013)

Socialism with a Northern Accent: radical traditions for modern times (2012)

COMING SOON FROM LANCASHIRE LOOMINARY

Moorlands, Memories and Reflections by Paul Salveson

A tribute to Allen Clarke's classic book on the Lancashire moorlands, *Moorlands and Memories*, first published in 1920. The book will explore some of the Lancashire moorlands visited by Clarke, on foot, bike and train, to see what has changed over the last century.

Expected publication date: June 2020

Lancashire Loominary

The Author

Paul Salveson was born in Bolton in October 1952 at what is now 'Royal Bolton Hospital' but back then was just 'Townley's'. He was brought up on Eustace Street, just off Crescent Road in Great Lever, spending much of his childhood hanging around the loco sheds. His dad worked at Walker's Tannery and mum spent time in various mills and factories, including The Bee Hive. He was educated at St Williams and then Thornleigh College (a good Catholic upbringing). He left school at 16 to do a year's course in Press Photography, then went on to do A Levels at Bolton Technical College. He read Sociology with History at Lancaster (but didn't drop out or attempt suicide). It has to be admitted he did a short spell at Horwich Loco Works in the Spring Smithy, before moving on to work as a railway guard at Blackburn, then signalman in Bolton.

He became a lay tutor for his union, the National Union of Railwaymen, before working for the Communist Party of Great Britain as its Area Secretary for Greater Manchester. He stood for the Communist Party in Burnden Ward (Bolton) scoring a derisory vote. He went on to do various jobs in community development and adult education before combining his transport interests with community work at Greater Manchester Council for Voluntary Services. He invented the idea of 'community rail' and set up the Association of Community Rail Partnerships in the mid-90s and became its general manager.

During his time in the Colne Valley (Huddersfield) he was involved in the Labour Party, becoming a councillor for a short time. He stood as the Yorkshire Party candidate for Colne Valley in the 2016 and did slightly better than when he stood for the CP back in the 1970s. He has worked in various senior rail industry roles and these days spends his time writing, 'playing trains', doing odd bits of consultancy and travelling around. He got his PhD in 'Lancashire Dialect Literature 1745-1935' from the University of Salford in 1992. In 2008 he was awarded an MBE for 'services to the railway industry'. He is a visiting professor at the universities of Huddersfield and Bolton. Regrets? None.

His personal website is **www.paulsalveson.org.uk**